John Phillips

GRITSTONE
PUBLISHING

John Phillips
Yorkshire's traveller through time
COLIN SPEAKMAN

Acknowledgements

Without the active support, encouragement and scholarly help of several individuals and organisations this book would not have happened. Dr John Knight, Vice President of the Yorkshire Geological Society, passionate about all things Yorkshire, was its inspiration, supported by Paul Hildreth, YGS President and his colleague Dr Andy Howard, YGS Secretary, who have both helped with images and text and worked with YGS colleagues to make this project possible. Equally, the Yorkshire Philosophical Society and Peter Hogarth, Rod Leonard and Bob Hale and their colleagues on the Council of the Yorkshire Philosophical Society have been brilliant proof-readers and offered myriad suggestions and checking of facts as well as access to their archives in the Borthwick Institute.

I am especially grateful for some generous financial support from both the Yorkshire Geological Society and the Yorkshire Philosophical Society to help with funding of this book.

Tom Lord has given me generous help in unravelling the complex story of Victoria Cave in Chapter Seven, as did Dr Tony Waltham with Chapter Five on the Mountain Limestone. Special thanks are due too to Dr Sarah King and Stuart Ogilvy of Yorkshire Museum for superb help with some key images in Chapters Two, Four and Five, to Simon Hedges and Jim Middleton of Scarborough Museum Trust for assistance with Chapter Three, Danielle Czerkaszyn for invaluable help with images from the Oxford University Natural History Museum, and to Mike Brockhurst, "The Walking Englishman", for use of some lovely photographs of some difficult to access places. Peter Woods shared some valued insights into Phillips and loan of the magnificent, largely unknown 1820 Sneaton Estate map, and Dorian Speakman went to some wild places to take some fine photographs.

Finally especial thanks to Lucy Frontani of Carnegie Book Production, who has done the inspirational design of the book, and to fellow Gritstone Co-op member Andrew Bibby, who did a heroic job proof-reading and editing my text, and Fleur Speakman who not only did the initial proof-read but has endured months of living with the spirit of Phillips on so many of our walks and excursions in the Dales, Wolds and Moors, and who has supported me in so many ways.

It goes without saying that whatever mistakes, misinterpretations and omissions are still there are entirely mine.

Colin Speakman   February 2020

WORLD
LAND
TRUST™

www.carbonbalancedpaper.com
CBP003152

Cover: Bust of John Phillips from the Oxford Museum of Natural History (photo © Oxford University Museum)
Page 7 portrait of John Phillips aged 50 by Thomas Maguire (© National Portrait Gallery)
Frontispiece: View of Walden and Pen Hill, Wensleydale, from Walden Head (author)

ISBN 978-0-9955609-8-7

Contents

Gritstone Publishing Co-operative is jointly owned by its members, some of
Britain's best-regarded authors writing about the countryside and the outdoors.
Look out for our other titles.

Long before my eyes rested on the
mountains of the north of England, the
mighty form of Ingleborough was engraved
in my imagination by many a vivid description

John Phillips

M & N HANHART IMP.

Foreword

It is impossible for anyone who takes even a moderately serious interest in the great natural beauty of Yorkshire, and its intimate relationship with topography, archaeology, geology, social history and industry, to fail to come upon some reference to John Phillips. However, the passage of time and the volume of modern communications and popular interpretation sometimes obscure the intellectual giants who set the foundations for our current understanding of the natural world. John Phillips was one of these giants. Importantly he identified himself with Yorkshire and the greater volume of his extensive field studies, expressed in magnificent works of observational and descriptive topography and geology, was performed within this county, forming subsequently the basis on which he achieved the stature of one of the major world figures in the development of geological science.

In this book Colin Speakman sets out to restore John Phillips to the forefront of popular recognition as an important world figure whose background and affiliation was deeply rooted in Yorkshire. Also, importantly, throughout his career his scientific work was accompanied by his commitment to widespread education, making the science of geology available to the general public irrespective of social status or gender. While there have been more academic studies on the life of John Phillips, this book unashamedly focuses on his social and scientific development in his adopted county of Yorkshire and his firmly expressed love of the physical landscape and the society which embraced him in York. Even from a modern perspective he remains an exemplar of a man

Great Fryup Dale, North York Moors (Andy Howard)

of science, whose basic criteria were founded on sound observation and careful and rational interpretation and thoughtful dissemination of his science to a wider and popular audience.

It has been a matter of great satisfaction to have been party, with other colleagues from the Yorkshire Geological Society, to the original conception of this book with its author Colin Speakman. Coinciding as it did with my term as 57th President of the Yorkshire Geological Society, this prompted reflection on some of the very eminent geologists who have preceded me in this post, and also on the "founding fathers" of the Society, who together have contributed so fundamentally to the understanding of the geology of our region. As recounted here, John Phillips was instrumental in the founding of our Society and also, at national level, to creating the British Association for the Advancement of Science, today the British Science Association. Phillips' influence, and particularly his enthusiasm to promote public interest in the geology of Yorkshire and the North of England, still reaches out to all of us who share this interest, whether at a professional or academic level or purely as an enthusiast. This book is long overdue as an introduction to the importance of the work of this, one of the major defining figures for the modern science of geology – who was undoubtedly "Made in Yorkshire".

John Knight

(President, Yorkshire Geological Society 2014–2016)

Introduction

Who was John Phillips?

Few people outside the specialist disciplines of geology, palaeontology and the history of science have ever heard of John Phillips, (1800–1874), yet he was one of the most influential scientific figures of the mid-nineteenth century. A remarkable polymath, he used his mastery of many different fields of science and his skills as a teacher, writer and administrator to help create much of the understanding of our world we take for granted today. The eminent Earth Science historian Professor Martin Rudwick has suggested that Phillips was "one of the world's leading palaeontologists" of his time.[1] To give just one illustration, it is Phillips' classification of the earliest stages of life on planet earth – *Palaeozoic*, *Mesozoic* and *Cainozoic* – that is still used today, worldwide. His prodigious intellectual energy, combined with a genial personality and liberal, humane values, influenced not only his own generation but those that followed. His ideas and perceptions still shape the way we see and talk about the natural world today.

This book does not attempt to be a biography of Phillips. This has been done by Jack Morrell in his masterly, and definitive, **John Phillips and the Business of Victorian Science** (2005).

The prime focus of this book is another important but perhaps neglected aspect of his genius, that of John Phillips the topographical writer.

He was one of the first great interpreters of the landscapes of his adopted county of Yorkshire where he lived and worked for over 30 years. This was during that period when England's countryside was first being made accessible for exploration by ordinary people on Britain's newly constructed railway network. In 1853 Phillips wrote one of the world's first railway guidebooks, exhorting his readers to alight at particular Yorkshire railway stations and explore on foot the landscape beyond to discover the region's many fascinating geological and historic features.

As one our first and finest outdoor writers, it is time that this aspect of the genius of John Phillips is celebrated.

Notes

1 Rudwick Martin (2014) *Earth's Deep History: how it was discovered and why it matters*. Chicago & London University of Chicago Press p220

The River Lune and Ingleborough from Hornby Castle
(after Turner)

1

The Strata Hunters – Uncle William and his Nephew John

Though born in Wiltshire and only coming up to Yorkshire in his late teens, John Phillips was able to make a significant contribution to the intellectual life of his adopted county.

Through his regular research, lecturing, and both academic and popular writing, Phillips contributed much to our modern understanding of the natural world. But he was also passionate about Yorkshire, particularly the great and fascinating landscape heritage of the uplands and the coast, its archaeology, history and architecture.

As he wrote in the Preface to his most celebrated book about the county, **The Rivers, Mountains and Sea Coast of Yorkshire,** from his earliest years he had been aware of the beauty of the landscape of the Yorkshire Dales and of the magnificent architecture of York Minster:

> *Long before my eyes rested on the mountains of the north of England, the mighty form of Ingleborough was engraved in my imagination by many a vivid description; and when I crossed the old Gothic bridge, and beheld the glorious Church, which is the pride and veneration of Yorkshire, it was but the realization of a long-indulged dream of boyhood.*[1]

York and Yorkshire were to become his physical home from his mid-twenties until his early fifties, and his spiritual home for the rest of his days.

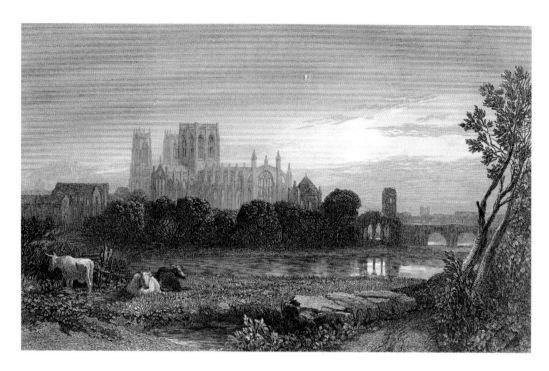

York Minster and ancient Bridge over the River Ouse (after Stansfield)

By his late twenties John was already the Senior Secretary of the
Yorkshire Philosophical Society, an organisation which became over the
next two decades one of the leading scientific societies in the north of
England. He was also the Keeper (curator) in York of one of the country's
first purpose built museums, and, before his thirtieth birthday, he had a
crucial role in the founding of the highly influential British Association
for the Advancement of Science – the "Parliament of Science" –
established in York in 1831.[2]

After professorships at both London University and Trinity College
Dublin and periods of work for the Geological Survey, Phillips was
appointed in 1853 as Assistant Reader of Geology of Oxford University.
He was to become Professor of Geology and to develop his department
into becoming one of the most significant scientific institutions in the
British Isles. He also was a leading figure in the building of the Oxford
Museum of Natural History, becoming its first Keeper.

The Strata Hunters – Uncle William and his Nephew John

This would have been a remarkable achievement for anyone born in even the most privileged station in society. But Phillips had no formal higher education. He came from a modest social background, was orphaned before his eighth birthday and had to cope with poverty and privations throughout his teenage years.

His life and career are of particular interest to a modern reader because John Phillips lived through that period of rapid economic and social change known as the Industrial Revolution This was a period of remarkable scientific discovery and technological development which produced rapidly changing ideas about mankind's relationship with the planet we inhabit and the wider universe, and with these discoveries an increasing awareness of the vastness of both space and time.

Phillips' uncle, the remarkable William "Strata" Smith (1769–1839), was one of the first generation of energetic individuals who were delivering that first Industrial Revolution. Smith was a highly regarded surveyor, and a canal and mining engineer, helping to bring about processes that were to lead to ever increasing mechanisation and mass production of goods and growth of trade in Britain during the end of the eighteenth and the first decades of the nineteenth century. Smith's pioneering geological researches were primarily undertaken as a way of predicting and understanding what lay under the surface soil, to allow mines to be sunk to exploit the mineral wealth to power and create the new industries. But the techniques which he and other pioneering surveyors and engineers developed allowed a new network of canals and navigations to be built over suitable water-retaining fault-free ground in order to transport bulk supplies of those raw materials. They would also enable the bulk export of manufactured goods to and from the new factories, mills and workshops through rapidly expanding ports such as Bristol, Liverpool, Hull and London.

William Smith

Smith's technique of stratigraphical analysis conveyed through geological maps were developed out of his need to be able to inform potential clients about the nature and characteristics of their land, and also where commercial rocks such as coal, minerals and building stone could be expected to be found. Palaeontology – the new science of fossil identification – was a valuable tool to establish the nature and character of underlying rock strata. Smith was the first mining surveyor to realise that the fossils found in each stratum give vital clues to the age and properties of that rock in similar locations throughout the British Isles. In the nineteenth century, the new science of geology enabled the exploitation of much of Britain's countryside for industrial development on a hitherto unimaginable scale.

John Phillips shared with his uncle William Smith the difficult circumstances of losing both his parents at an early age. John was born on Christmas Day in 1800 in the village of Marden in Wiltshire, son of William Smith's sister Elizabeth, and an assistant excise officer, also named John Phillips. Their first child Ann had died in infancy. A second surviving daughter, also named Ann(e) – but usually spelled with an e – was born three years later and a second son Jenkin followed in 1806.

In 1808 twin tragedies struck the family. John Phillips senior died suddenly in January, to be followed by Elizabeth in July, leaving the three children orphaned.

William Smith must have seen the parallels with his own life and was quick to rescue the little family. They lived with him for a few weeks, but his wife Mary was not well enough to look after three children. So little Jenkin was put under the care of his uncle Daniel Smith and the two older children were sent to another uncle, John Smith, who farmed at Broadfield situated between Midford and Hinton Charterhouse, near Bath, in north east Somerset.

In 1809, when he was eight years old, John Phillips junior was sent by his uncle to a boarding school run by David Thomas Arnot at Holt in Wiltshire. Smith paid his fees there for five years.

John was an exceptionally bright lad and by the standards of its time, Arnot's school seems to have been an especially good institution. As well as the usual rudiments of education, he was given a good grounding in mathematics, including algebra and geometry, and acquired excellent skills in Latin and French and in drawing. He also learned some Greek. All were to prove extremely useful both in helping his uncle and in his own scientific work in future years. John was an avid reader and was also given a small microscope which he used to examine plants, insects and shells collected locally on walks and rambles.

When in 1814 growing financial difficulties made it impossible for William Smith to continue to pay his nephew's school fees, he arranged for John to spend a year with his friend Reverend Benjamin Richardson. John, only thirteen years old, stayed at the Rectory at Farleigh Hungerford, some six miles from Bath, living and studying with the family and having access to Richardson's library and extensive fossil collections.

It was a crucial period in John Phillips' life. In his study of Phillips' life and career, Jack Morrell is surely right in suggesting that the influence of this gentle, humanistic, scientific clergyman was crucial both in terms of awakening a growing intellectual passion in the young man and in suggesting a model of tolerant, compassionate Christianity that Phillips was to follow throughout his life.[3]

Benjamin Richardson

Empirical observation and inductive reason were for Richardson, and later for Phillips, ultimately a means of discovering the truth about a rich, beautiful and ordered Universe and its all-powerful and all-seeing Creator.

Richardson spent up to an hour a day with his protégé during his stay at Farleigh, enthusing and inspiring him, discussing his uncle's theories of stratigraphy and explaining the crucial role of the fossil evidence. He also taught him the importance of classification of information to record and interpret the structure of botanical and palaeontological specimens. It was an informal but precious tutelage that was going to shape the growth of a remarkable intellect:

> He experienced for the first time an environment of academic
> calm and detachment, and at the same time he came under
> the direct superintendence of one who was prepared to devote
> unstinted attention to a willing and talented pupil. He was
> given the freedom of a large and richly varied private library, the
> resources of which were reinforced with frequent borrowings from
> the lending libraries of Bath and London. He was encouraged to
> sort, classify, and name the contents of Richardson's fossil cabinet
> and other natural history collections, using, under guidance, the
> whole range of reference works available. He was set to work to
> improve his natural ability as an artist by copying the excellent
> drawings of fossils prepared by the Rev. Joseph Townsend for his
> work The Character of Moses[4]

John Phillips benefited hugely from absorbing the immense practical engineering and surveying skills of his uncle and from Smith's ability to apply and structure the knowledge so obtained to the new science of geology.[5] But as the geologist and Wiltshire historian James Maxwell Edmonds has suggested:

> It was however to Benjamin Richardson that Phillips was
> dependent for his scientific discipline and instruction, and
> to both his instructors, he was ever ready to acknowledge his
> personal debt.[6]

Richardson would continue to inspire and sustain him through difficult and challenging times ahead.

In 1844, five years after Smith's death in Northampton en route to an Annual Meeting of the British Association for the Advancement of Science, John Phillips as Smith's "nephew and pupil" published his fine account of his uncle's life, **Memoirs of William Smith**. The volume was also dedicated to the memory of Richardson "the loved associate of his early studies" and the book included his silhouette portrait.

In 1815 John Phillips moved back for a short time to stay with his uncle at his home and work base at Tucking Mill House, near Midford in

Somerset. They soon moved to
Smith's rather grand house at
15 Buckingham Street, close to
The Strand in London where he
worked as Smith's desperately
needed assistant and apprentice.
This area of London was at that
time a centre for the city's rapidly
growing printing, publishing and
map making trade.

It must have been a tough
challenge to the youngster who
had to become the main personal
support to his brilliant but often
eccentric and wayward uncle.
It would have been a lonely
existence separated from other friends of his age. He was also separated
from his beloved sister Anne and they were not able to meet again for
several years.

John Phillips acted as Smith's amanuensis in dealing with
correspondence. He helped to catalogue and label Smith's massive fossil
collection; his fluency in Latin and French, of which his uncle had little or
no knowledge, proved crucial in giving the fossils their correct botanical
names and in translating key texts such as the newly published work of
the French zoologist and geologist Cuvier. He was soon helping to draw
plans and maps for canals and other projects.

Within a couple of years he taught himself techniques of the new art of
lithography, an engraving technique using wax-covered stone – usually
a fine quality smooth limestone – over which water-based colour inks
could be spread. This was a way of printing and over-printing colour
images for maps or illustrations, for example of fossils. It was a technique

that had been developed in Germany by Alois Senefelder in the 1790s but was now out of patent. This was a far quicker and less expensive way of printing maps than traditional engraving. The teenage Phillips was soon producing some fine lithographed drawings of fossils specimens.[7] He was also learning to use, mend and even make a variety of tools and instruments used for surveying. These practical skills developed out of necessity but were to prove very useful in his later career.

Lithography was used in later years by Smith and Phillips in preparing the series of 21 county maps of England which Smith saw as a necessary way of earning his living. When times became especially hard, producing lithographic prints and drawings for their own and other people's publications also enabled Phillips to raise badly needed cash to sustain his uncle and himself.

Between 1817 and 1819 John accompanied his uncle as his assistant on his regular journeys around England on surveying work. In 1817 they visited the coast of Whitby and Scarborough for the planned county map of Yorkshire. There were also extended visits, mostly on foot, to both Norfolk and Suffolk and the Forest of Dean. There was a journey in the winter of 1818/9, after an absence of ten years, to William Smith's birthplace at Churchill, Oxfordshire. They visited William's brother John who was now a prosperous local farmer – a fact that must have evoked painful reflections for William. Presumably they also met John Phillips' younger brother Jenkin.

Several visits in 1818 and 1819 were again made to Yorkshire, surveying for a major new canal scheme linking the River Don and River Aire in the West Riding, where for the first time John could see for himself the great Magnesian Limestone belt that runs through central Yorkshire from the Midlands to the Durham coast. However the canal scheme, which might have resulted in Smith being appointed as its well-paid Surveyor, did not go ahead owing to opposition in Parliament from the rival Aire-Calder Navigation Company. Another trip took uncle and nephew for the first time into Swaledale, with an intriguing visit to the Auld Gang lead mines near Gunnerside, then at the height of their productive activity.

However a traumatic series of events was about to occur that would change the lives of William Smith and John Phillips for ever, and which

William's Smith's 1815 Map of England and Wales
(©British Geological Survey – Crown copyright)

Auld Gang Smelt Mill in Swaledale, visited by Smith and Phillips in 1819 when the lead mines were fully operational (Walking Englishman)

would provide the reason for them to bring their combined talents to the North of England, and to Yorkshire in particular.

The source of the issue lay in Smith's greatest single achievement which should have been his greatest triumph – and source of financial success.

For some years Smith had realised that a Geological Map of England and Wales indicating what type of rocks and therefore minerals lay in which areas of the country would be of huge economic value for landowners and industrialists. Ironically this great, public-spirited idea was to have disastrous consequences for its author.

The map took years of meticulous work to achieve. He spent time travelling, often at some considerable expense, often to obscure places, surveying the land in detail, seeking out and recording outcrops, quarries, mineshafts and fossils. This was time which he might more sensibly have devoted to his commercial and cash paying contracts.

The map, once achieved, was and remains a masterpiece.[8] Even though it has been frequently revised and improved, the broad divisions of rock systems across England, Wales and into part of Scotland, first identified and coloured by Smith, remain remarkably unchanged. Some of Smith's chosen colouring system still survives to some degree in many modern geological maps.

The map was eventually published in 1815 for Smith by the London publisher John Cary, and Smith hoped that its rapid sales would amply repay him for the huge time and energy spent on producing it.

It was not to be. Sales were slower than he had hoped. Worse, within a short time, the map was in part plagiarised by George Ballas Greenough, President to the Geological Society,[9] and a rival version was published, which undercut Smith on price. To be fair, Greenough's map also had a number of improvements to Smith's original, obtained by using the Society's many regional contacts with local knowledge and surveying skills.[10]

But the key problem was the national economic depression. At that time of post-Napoleonic War economic hardship, there was less money available for Britain's landed gentry to invest in new buildings or speculative industrial schemes. The offers of work which Smith had anticipated did not materialise.

Being preoccupied with his great map, Smith had been unfortunate and rash both by neglecting his core business and in not seeking new contracts with different clients. As his nephew was later to recall:

> Geology had kept him poor by consuming all his professional gains; the neglect of his employers too often left these unpaid; in such circumstances one unfortunate step was ruin and that step was made.[11]

This was the investment in a quarry and railway scheme near Bath; it turned out the stone in the quarry was of poorer quality than Smith had predicted. The economic recession had also reduced demand for building stone of any quality.

In 1816 he was forced to sell his precious collection of fossils – 2,657 carefully categorised specimens from 693 animal and plant species – to the British Museum for an extremely low price.[12]

Things worsened. On 11th June 1819 bailiffs arrived outside Smith's house in Buckingham Street in central London. Smith was arrested and flung into King's Bench Debtors' Prison in Southwark, where he was forced to remain for eighty nights before finally being discharged, enough of his debts having been repaid by the sale of what few goods and chattels remained from his estate.

It was an extraordinary, and disgraceful, way for a nation to treat a man later to be dubbed the Father of English Geology, whose life's work was going to have a profound impact on earth sciences worldwide.

Fortunately for Smith, he had his nephew, John Phillips to help him find a way though this crisis.

On the evening of August 31st, William Smith, just released from prison, disgraced and penniless, left London with his wife Mary Ann who was suffering from mental illness at this time, and his eighteen year old nephew. They caught the Northern Mail, the overnight coach from Holborn, to the small North Riding market town of Northallerton, a journey that took them three days.

The object of their long and uncomfortable journey north was quite simply to find work. Smith probably wanted to get as far away as he could from London and his horrific experience in prison. With just *"a few papers, his hammer and acid bottle, magnifying glass and compass, a theodolite and chain"*[13] William Smith and John Phillips began their journey to Yorkshire, a journey that was not only to change their lives but have a profound impact on the progress of scientific thought.

Smith's imprisonment and the events leading up to it in 1819 are carefully and euphemistically passed over by Phillips in his 1844 **Memoirs of William Smith**, no doubt because of the shame of the experience. However Phillips does say:

> *on the abstract geologist the blow fell with stunning effect.*
>
> *From this time for seven years he became a wanderer in the North of England, rarely visiting London except when drawn thither by the professional engagements which still, even in his loneliest retirements, were pressed upon him, and yielded him an irregular, contracted and fluctuating income.*[14]

Phillips gives a fascinating account of their journeys over the next few years as they took some quite extraordinary excursions. Having first arrived in Yorkshire in 1819, they began a series of journeys through the Midlands and North of England to seek work or to fulfil contracts,

Fourteenth-century village inn in Gretton, Northamptonshire, where Smith and Phillips stayed in 1819

or, between engagements, to carry out detailed surveys for future map projects. They spent time in the Midlands staying in cheap inns and lodging houses for days or even weeks at a time. One of the first of these trips was a walking and surveying tour from Lincolnshire to Oxfordshire, as Phillips wryly remarks: *Mr Smith having perhaps more than usual leisure.*

The journey could have its depressing yet more enjoyable moments. Staying in the little village inn in Gretton, in Rockingham Forest, Northamptonshire Phillips noted:

> "Whatever may now be the accommodations in this village, they were very wretched in 1819 (December) but the odd stories of supernatural beings and incredible frights which were assembled at the little inn greatly amused Mr Smith and reminded him of exactly parallel tales which circulated round Whichwood Forest in his boyhood".[15]

They continued to Kettering, noticing on the road the peculiar character of the Northamptonshire oolite where it outcropped. From here, as William was overtired or had sprained a muscle, they had to hire a horse-drawn chaise, which would have been a drain on their limited budget. This still gave them time to note different rocks and fossils as they travelled, including a large ammonite lying by a tree on the roadside left there by Smith as it was *"too large and inconvenient for the pocket"*. Smith had remembered exactly where it was the last time he passed along this road and sure enough it was still there.[16] In Oxford they met the Reverend William Buckland (1784–1846), Fellow of the Royal Society and Reader in Mineralogy at Oxford University, who was later to achieve further international fame by undertaking investigations of prehistoric animal remains at Kirkdale Cave, work that was to have a significant impact on the lives of both Smith and Phillips.

Throughout their journeys William and John were constantly recording, in notebooks or on maps, the observations they had made.

For John Phillips this was perhaps the most remarkable tutelage any bright and intelligent individual could have had – working closely with a great field geologist like Smith, absorbing his ideas, his methodology and his philosophy. The ageing Smith also now had an energetic and enthusiastic companion, someone his intellectual equal, the son he never had.

After Smith's spell in debtors' prison and the flight to Yorkshire, the relationship between the two men had subtly changed. Increasingly it was young John Phillips looking after his uncle, though no doubt Phillips let his uncle feel that whatever decisions that had to be made were entirely his.

In 1820 they travelled and spent some time back in Yorkshire, going to Ferrybridge and on to Whitby, finding paid work whenever they could. One such commission was the preparation of a detailed map of the Sneaton Estate, near Sleights in the Esk Valley near Whitby, for landowner James Wilson of Sneaton Castle. The map shows in great detail the individual field and farm boundaries, woods, streams, nature of the terrain, coal pits, lime kilns and a small "railway" (early tramway) between a coal pit and a lime kiln, presumably to produce slaked lime for improvement of otherwise acid soils on the estate.

The "romantic and delightful" town of Scarborough was their next destination, partly in hope of helping Mary Smith whose mental state was getting ever more troubling. Scarborough with its beautiful coastal surroundings and rich geological interest pleased all of them, and what was particularly fortunate was that they were able to attend a meeting of a group of enthusiastic amateur scientists keen to build a museum in the town and to establish a new Scarborough Philosophical Society. This was a project that was eventually to become important to both William and John.

Further trips followed through the coalfields of the West Riding, again gathering vital information for the proposed Yorkshire maps. At Cadeby, near Doncaster, the two geologists speculated on where a better water

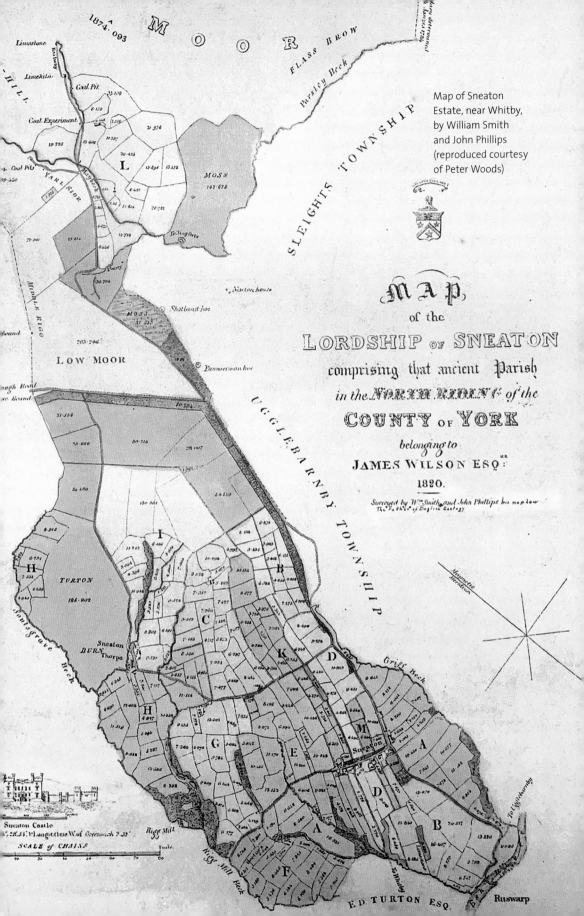

Map of Sneaton Estate, near Whitby, by William Smith and John Phillips (reproduced courtesy of Peter Woods)

MAP of the LORDSHIP of SNEATON comprising that ancient Parish in the NORTH RIDING of the COUNTY of YORK belonging to JAMES WILSON ESQ[r] 1820.

Surveyed by W[m] Smith and John Phillips his nephew The Father of English Geology

supply could be sourced, and they were able to make more detailed observations of the local Magnesian Limestone beds.

By now John was perfectly capable of making independent surveys on his own. He travelled to Doncaster, Roche Abbey, Gringley-on-the-Hill and Gainsborough "*to assist Mr Smith's researches*". The four detailed maps of Yorkshire that these and other researches contributed to were finally published in 1821.[17]

Phillips later described in some detail the methodology of "strata hunting" that the two itinerant surveyors employed to survey an area, with Smith and Phillips walking in two parallel lines through a given area, then meeting to compare notes.

> *Two lines of operation were drawn through the country which required to be surveyed for the completing such maps, or rather such Parts of maps as had been inevitably left imperfect. On one of these Mr Smith moved with the due deliberation of a commander-in-chief; the other was traversed by his more active sub-altern, who found the means often to cross from his own parallel to report progress at headquarters. This mode of "strata hunting" was not necessarily expensive; it was besides extremely agreeable and effective, and was faithfully executed in peregrinations which lasted six months, and permitted one of the parties to walk over 2,000 miles of ground, and preserve memoranda of almost every mile along that line.*[18]

This was an incredible physical achievement by any standards.

These "*peregrinations*" of 1821 also led them back into Lincolnshire, Leicestershire and Derbyshire. Then came what must have been a powerful experience for Phillips, a walk from what is now known as the Peak District of Derbyshire to the Lake District, again often working in the two-line formation, notebooks in hand. Phillips describes how the many attractive landscape features on their long ramble along the Pennines from Todmorden, Burnley, Colne and Skipton were soon "*eclipsed by the bolder scenes round Settle, Giggleswick, Ingleton, Kirkby Lonsdale and Kendal*"[19]

A glimpse of the summit of Pen-y-Ghent from Giggleswick, a view first seen by John Phillips in 1821 when travelling north with his uncle on the road to Kendal (author)

Smith's and Phillips' researches then led them north from Kirkby Lonsdale to Sedbergh, through the Crook of Lune to the Shap Fells and eventually to Bowness on Windermere. From there they went via Newby Bridge to Ennerdale and then by Buttermere to Keswick where they met the celebrated Lakeland geologist Jonathan Otley, with whom they compared notes. Phillips noted how:

> *Mr Smith's attentive eyes embraced every curious object in nature or art, and found perpetual occupation for the pen or pencil of his willing assistant*[20]

This trip led to the preparation of several more of the County Maps, eventually to be published by John Cary, for Cumberland, Westmorland and Lancashire. Also produced was a single sheet map of the Lake District, no doubt produced with an eye on the emerging tourist market.

Their next area of cartographical research was to be the North Pennines, and they travelled over Hartside Pass to visit the Alston lead mines where they met and talked with local miners. They then continued eastwards through the North Pennines into Northumberland and through the Cheviots to Wooler, returning via Newcastle and Durham finally to Ripon and Harrogate and Leeds. Here they met members of the Leeds Philosophical and Literary Society to whom William gave a well-received lecture on the geology of Yorkshire. Following another "visit on business" to the lead mines of Swaledale, the duo terminated their year with a walk from Leeds to Nottingham.

Early in 1822 they also had a "professional journey" on paid consultancy work to Durham where Smith was able to advise Colonel Thomas Braddyll who had previously consulted him on potential copper workings around Conishead Priory near Ulverston. Smith suggested that the land Braddyll owned in County Durham had great promise. This eventually led to Braddyll opening the great South Hetton Colliery near Easington, near the coast, which was to become one of the largest and most profitable coalmines in England.

Sadly this was of little benefit to Smith. As his nephew was to record:

> "yet the execution of this grand scheme, for which Mr Smith has strenuously contended, was entrusted to others.[21]

So their journeys in search of other work, paid surveying, estate management or drainage work, had to continue. They headed west again in order to complete Smith's geological maps of the north west of England. Later in that year, 1822, they travelled together to find lodgings in what they hoped would be a convenient location for this purpose, the small town of Kirkby Lonsdale in Westmorland, on the edge of the limestone country of the Yorkshire Dales and conveniently close to the Lake District.

This was to open a new chapter of their lives.

Notes

1   Phillips John *1853 The Rivers Mountains and Sea Coast of Yorkshire* London: John Murray p vii

2   Orange A.D. 1973 *Philosophers and Provincials The Yorkshire Philosophical Society from 1822–1844* York: YPS pp32–39

3   Morrell Jack 2005 *John Phillips and the Business of Victorian Science* Aldershot: Ashgate pp24–25

4   Edmonds JM 1982 *The First Apprentice Geologist* in Wiltshire Archaeological and Natural History Magazine 76 p153–4

5   Morgan Nina 2019 *Growing up a Geologist* – Geology Today, 35 Issue 5 (October 2019) pp179–185

6   *Ibid.* p154

7   Phillips John edjted by Twyman M. 2016 *John Phillips's Lithographic Notebook* 2016 (Printing Historical Society London)

8   Winchester Simon 2001 *The Map that changed the World* London: Viking Press pp194–223

9   *Ibid.* pp230–240

10 Hawley Duncan, Lam Caroline 2020 *Greenough's World* in Geoscientist February 2020 pp16–192

11 Phillips John 1844 *Memoirs of William Smith* London: John Murray p78

12 Winchester Simon 2001 *op. cit.* pp247–252

13 *Ibid.* p265

14 Phillips John 1844 *op. cit.* p90

15 *Ibid.* p92

16 *Ibid.* p91–2

17 *Ibid.* p96

18 *Ibid.* p96

19 *Ibid.* p98

20 *Ibid.* p99

21 *Ibid.* p102

Yorkshire Museum, designed by William Wilkins and opened in 1830 (author)

2

The Yorkshire Philosophical
Society and the Yorkshire Museum

For three years, between 1819 and 1822, John Phillips had accompanied his uncle William Smith as his assistant as they made *"long and laborious wanderings"* in undertaking geological surveying through the northern counties of England, combining Smith's work on his maps of the English counties with any available *"professional engagements"* as itinerant surveyors, canal and drainage engineers when and wherever work would lead them, staying in cheap lodging houses and inns, with only a modest and very fluctuating income to support their physical needs.

In 1822 came that very pleasant interlude in the lives of the two travellers. They had travelled from Durham to visit Kirkby Lonsdale, in Westmorland, on the south western corner of the Yorkshire Dales. It was, as it is now, a small but attractive country market town, close to a historic stone bridge over the River Lune, with a view up-river to the fells that was later to be celebrated by art historian and philosopher John Ruskin as one of the finest in England. This was a place convenient to spend some time finishing Smith's Lancashire and Westmorland maps. But there was much to explore locally of special geological interest and perhaps new opportunities for work.

Whilst Smith was employing his somewhat eccentric habit of identifying the nature of the local rock outcrops by judging the hardness of pebbles by biting them against his own teeth, he was observed by some local stone masons in the town. They pointed Smith towards someone further

Market Street, Kirkby Lonsdale as it is today (author)

along the lane who they reckoned, with his little hammer and specimen bag, was "of the same trade".

This individual was no less than the great Dentdale geologist and Woodwardian Professor of Cambridge University Adam Sedgwick (1785–1873). This was a chance meeting of two of the most influential geological minds of the century, who were quick to compare notes – Smith was able to describe the organic remains in what was then called Greywacke, or Silurian/Ordovician rocks, that they had both observed in nearby quarries. Phillips records[1] how the two eminent men walked some distance together along the Kendal road, the Professor then continuing on horseback to Low Furness. By chance, Phillips had also met Sedgwick a few days previously at High Force in Teesdale. Sedgwick was later to become a great champion of Smith, presenting him with the Geological Society's first Wollaston Medal in 1831, coining the phrase "The Father of English Geology" to describe his friend.

For the first time since leaving London in despair, William Smith felt he was in a sanctuary where he could stay and enjoy a degree of peace:

feeding all the best qualities of his mind by calm meditations,
not unmixed with the poetic impressions which seem
perpetually to haunt the romantic banks of the Lune.[2]

Smith and Phillips took temporary root in the town, enjoying rest and freedom and doing a significant number of rambles from their base *"in a circle of 15 miles"*. This enabled them to collect material for the completion of their Westmorland and Lancashire maps, and to make corrections and additions to the Yorkshire maps. These included details of the fascinating and complex slate rocks which are visible along the southern slopes of Ingleborough which they were able to note and fully record. The geology of the area was especially rich in interest for the co-workers, and the pair were soon exploring and collecting fossils from the Hutton Roof Crags and Kirkby Moor areas, occasionally enjoying longer excursions into Cumberland or even as far as Durham returning via Hell Gill and the summit of Wild Boar Fell – a challenging hike.

Adam Sedgwick aged 47 (Samuel Cousins – Wellcome Library collection)

These excursions and related field research with his uncle were invaluable for Phillips' later work in Yorkshire, most especially his great work on the Yorkshire Dales Carboniferous Limestones, which was to absorb him in the decade ahead. He was able to examine the line of fracture of the earth's surface, with up to two thousand feet of displacement in places along the main fault and its many branches – known as the Craven Fault – that defines the southern boundaries of the Yorkshire Dales. He also noted the layers of thinner limestone high on the slopes of Ingleborough which he was later to name the Yoredale series of limestones.

They had time during the winter of 1822–3 to visit the copper and zinc mines around Hesket Newmarket in the northern Lake District, exploring mine workings and smelting houses. They were fascinated by

Wild Boar Fell (author)

the variety of minerals in the ancient rocks of the Lake District hills. The two of them even set up a small smelting furnace in the garden of their lodgings to experiment with various mineral samples they had gathered.

During their stay in Kirkby Lonsdale, early in 1824, a local resident, Edward Wilson, requested William's help to improve the town's water supply from springs in the limestone close to the town. Soon afterwards, this led to Smith being introduced to a relative of Wilson, a Dr Matthew Allen of York. Dr Allen on his return to York mentioned his meeting with Smith to the newly formed Yorkshire Philosophical Society, which had been established in York in 1822 to deal with recent discoveries of organic remains in Kirkdale Cave, near Kirkbymoorside on the edge of the North York Moors.

Having met Smith and been enthused by Smith's amazing geological knowledge, Dr Allen recommended Smith to the Society as a lecturer, and the President of the Society, the Reverend William Venables Vernon, invited William Smith to give a course of lectures on geology to the Society for a suitable fee.

As Phillips remarked, perhaps slightly dryly, though "*he had never lectured, he had for half his life been talking about geology*".[3]

William Smith accepted the offer immediately. New maps were coloured, new sections drawn, and fossils collected, some extra ones even borrowed from his old friend Benjamin Richardson. He also suggested that his nephew could help to arrange the Society's geological collection so that their fossils could be organised as his original collection now in the vaults of the British Museum was, in both stratigraphic and systematic order"[4]

When John Phillips set off in 1824 to walk to York via Leeds to join his uncle, he could have had little idea of how much this visit was going to change both their lives.

The reasons for the invitation originated in a discovery in July 1821 by local quarrymen of a large quantity of mysterious bones in a cave in a quarry on a steep hillside above Hodge Beck at Kirkdale, Kirkbymoorside. Local fossil hunters and antiquarians were soon extremely interested in the finds.

Top: Kirkdale Cave and Quarry as it was in 1820
(from *Reliquiae Diluvianae* – Yorkshire Museum collection)
Above: Kirkdale Cave as it is today (author)

This led, in December 1821, to a visit by William Buckland, by then Reader in Geology at Oxford University. Buckland was fascinated by what he found. He was able to prove:

> "*that this could not be the relics of animals washed there by Noah's flood, but were the fossilised skeletons of animals which had lived in those caves. But this was Yorkshire not the African savannah. Buckland suggested that antediluvian Europe was inhabited by animals such as hyena, elephants and other unfamiliar creatures*"[5]

Buckland was later able to demonstrate in a quite spectacular way, by using living hyenas from a local travelling circus able to crunch bones in an identical manner to replicate the tooth damage evident on the fossil specimens, that this had been an ancient hyena den. He was to identify fossil bones not just of hyena, but of many other creatures – bears, elephant, rhinoceros and elks, whose carcases had been dragged into the den for consumption, and whose well chewed bones were eventually covered with gravels and mud.

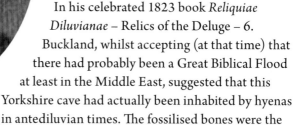

William Buckland

In his celebrated 1823 book *Reliquiae Diluvianae* – Relics of the Deluge – 6. Buckland, whilst accepting (at that time) that there had probably been a Great Biblical Flood at least in the Middle East, suggested that this Yorkshire cave had actually been inhabited by hyenas in antediluvian times. The fossilised bones were the remains of these hyenas and of the animals they had eaten and brought into the cave, rather than animals that had perished in the Flood and been carried to the cave by surging waters, as had first been thought[6].

Inspired by Buckland's work, on 7th December 1822 three amateur naturalists from York, James Atkinson, a surgeon, William Salmond, a retired army Colonel, and Anthony Thorpe a lawyer, who had each collected and stored quite a few of the Kirkdale fossil bones, met in

Atkinson's home in Lendal, York, with a view to setting up a Yorkshire Philosophical Society. This was not an organisation concerned with abstract philosophy in the modern sense, rather "Natural Philosophy" – the study of nature and the physical universe, in effect everything we would now call "Natural Science." This was to be a purely scientific society.

One of their first acts was to invite Reverend William Venables Vernon (1789–1871), son of the Archbishop of York and already a noted and gifted local amateur geologist, chemist and naturalist, to join them. Vernon duly did. William Vernon's father, Edward Vernon, the Archbishop, took the name Harcourt when he succeeded to the family estates in 1830. From that time his son William also took the name William Vernon Harcourt.

William Vernon soon became their Chairman and later President. At their second meeting a week later the Society issued a Prospectus.[7] Their aims included the setting up of a Scientific Library and a Museum to display their own Kirkdale and other fossil and mineral collections, and which would be *"open to every subject of scientific curiosity"*. There would also be a *"Repository of Antiquities in which the city abounds and of Geological Specimens of which no district in England can furnish a greater variety than the County of York"*. But equally significantly the *"Illustrations of Geology"* would be a *"principal design"* of the proposed Museum.[8]

Ouse Bridge with the building, right, which housed the Yorkshire Philosophical Society's first Museum (from Baines, History, Directory and Gazetteer of City of York 1822)

The historian Allan Chapman has written of what he described as "*the Grand Amateur Tradition of Science in Georgian and Victorian Britain*", gentlemen of means whose income and wealth allowed them time to indulge in their taste for the arts and leisured scientific activity. This included fossil and mineral collecting which often led to a more serious and structured interest in the new science of geology. As Chapman points out:

> It is hardly surprising, therefore, that unlike today, being a "professional" scientist in early Victorian Britain carried with it … a connotation of servility rather than one of kudos.[9]

York in particular may not have been a wealthy manufacturing city in the 1820s but it had a rich rural hinterland, dominated by great country estates. No less than fifty such estates flourished within a ten mile radius of the city, a potential source not only of membership but of donations for books and scientific equipment.[10] Admission to Membership at £5 – more than two weeks wages for even a skilled workman – and £1 annually thereafter in effect excluded most of the lower orders, added to the fact that new members needed two sponsors who were already members to join. Women were not invited to become Members at a time when "*contemporary notions of propriety took precedence over maximising potential income*",[11] though they could in later years subscribe in return for certain privileges.

Stimulus for a Philosophical Society in York also came from the realisation that similar scientific and literary bodies were flourishing in the new manufacturing centres of Manchester, Sheffield, Leeds and Hull. As in York, their membership came from local landowners, higher paid professional people such as lawyers, and also a very significant number of scholar-clergymen. A position in the church, and with it a regular salary, was one way a young man of the early nineteenth century with intellectual aspirations and the right social background could progress his wider literary or scientific aspirations. There were also representatives of the newly wealthy manufacturers – owners of factories, workshops or mines who had both the wealth and leisure to enjoy intellectual pursuits. In addition there were men from Dissenter and Quaker backgrounds, such as Unitarian Minister Charles Wellbeloved, denied access to Universities because of their faith, but thirsty for knowledge and intellectual progress.[12]

So early in 1824 William Smith travelled to York to meet the Society's President William Venables Vernon and its two Secretaries Dr George Goldie and F.J. Copsie. He set out before them an ambitious prospectus for a course of lectures, covering the principles of geology and stratigraphy, palaeontology and related areas of knowledge, the full details of which are included in John Phillips' **Memoirs of William Smith**– though as Phillips wryly says, *"but it was not to be supposed that the formula was rigidly adhered to"*.[13]

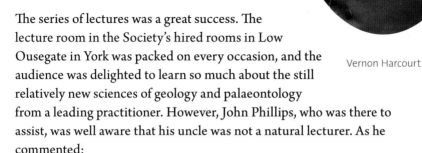

Vernon Harcourt

The series of lectures was a great success. The lecture room in the Society's hired rooms in Low Ousegate in York was packed on every occasion, and the audience was delighted to learn so much about the still relatively new sciences of geology and palaeontology from a leading practitioner. However, John Phillips, who was there to assist, was well aware that his uncle was not a natural lecturer. As he commented:

> *A certain abstractness of mind, generated by long and solitary meditation, a habit of flowing out his own thoughts into means of research even while engaged in explaining simplest of facts, continually broke into the symmetry of Mr Smith's lectures. Slight matters, things curious in themselves but not clearly commonly associated with the general purpose of the lecture, swelled into excrescences, stopped the growth of parts which were more important in themselves, or necessary to connect with observations into an intelligible and satisfactory system.*[14]

But Phillips had to concede that that there was a *"charm thrown over the discourse"* by the diagrams, the total absence of all technical trifling and above all *"the simplicity and honesty of the man"*.

The lectures were so well received and attended that Smith's remuneration for the series was increased from £50 to £60 and the Society still made a profit of £23.

A more secure source of income came to Phillips when early in 1824 he was paid £20 by the Yorkshire Philosophical Society to arrange their collection of over 2,000 fossils gifted or loaned to the Society by myriad collectors, in their correct stratigraphical order using Smithian principles. This was to form a central part of the Society's newly established Museum in Low Ousegate. In doing this work he gained additional insight and confirmation of the similarities between the palaeontology of local strata and those of the south of England. But he also had access to the Society's equally recently established library which already contained a fine collection of donated books and scientific papers by leading figures of the day.

Importantly, he had time for his own research and fieldwork. In April 1824 for example he joined his friend Edward George for a geological walking tour from York to Leeds, continuing to Nidderdale and Wharfedale, which included a visit to lead mines and caves around Greenhow Hill, close to what are now known as the Stump Cross Cavern Show Caves.

As he was later to write:

> One of the most interesting caves I ever saw was opened in the course of lead-mining at Greenhow Hill. In 1825 (sic) when I reached it by a miner's climbing shaft, it has much the appearance of a Franconian bear cave – dust on the floor, stalactites of great size and brilliant beauty everywhere depending from the roof. It was however soon robbed of its sparry ornaments by tasteless visitors and greedy miners and must now be mentioned as one of the lost wonders of Yorkshire.[15]

Though officially Stump Cross Caverns were only discovered by William and Mark Newbold in 1860, Phillips' description seems to closely match the original appearance of the caves, then only accessed through lead mine workings. Happily there were other parts of the system rich in stalactites largely undamaged which now form part of the Show Cave. But Phillips was quite right in predicting its importance for fossil bones. Reindeer and wolverine were discovered there in 1922.

Phillips and George had also taken with them a mountain barometer which enabled the user to calculate the height of nearby hilltops from barometric readings. Phillips used George's instrument, but with his lifelong fascination with measuring instruments and his practical skills he was quick to build his own version. This proved an invaluable tool in recording accurate measurements of the height of coastal cliffs and moorland summits on his frequent coastal and inland walks.

So well had Phillips' excellent and detailed work with the Yorkshire Philosophical Society's fossil collection been received, that from 1826 the Society appointed him as their first Keeper of the Museum and Draughtsman, at a salary of £60 per annum. This salary had to be personally underwritten by the Council Members in sums varying from £5 from William Vernon, £2 from Charles Wellbeloved and £1 from other members.[16]

He was also asked to give lectures. As the first Annual Report for 1824 (published in 1825 and clearly including recent items of new interest early in 1825) records:

> *Encouraged by the success which attended the Lectures in the*
> *last Spring, the Council has made proposals for two courses to*
> *be delivered in the present year, in the months of February and*
> *March ... Mr J. Phillips, a gentleman with whose attainments*
> *the Meeting are well acquainted, and to whose intelligence and*

Inside Stump Cross Caverns, Nidderdale (© Stump Cross)

industry the Society has been greatly indebted, has undertaken
a short course of Lectures on the Primitive Rocks and
Organised Fossils, supplementary to those which were delivered
in 1824 by his relative Mr Smith.[17]

These were Phillips' first public lectures for the Society. His first lectures as actual Keeper of the Museum formed part of a short course on geology given a year later.

The modest salary as Keeper however also reflected the fact that Phillips enjoyed the vitally important freedom to pursue his other research, lecturing and writing. Hours of attendance at the museum were only 10am to 4pm three days of the week and he was to be granted leave of absence for up to 3 months a year for research visits and lecture tours, which could be well paid at up to £7 per lecture. This meant he could go on extended lecture tours to other Philosophical Societies as far away as Leeds, Hull, Scarborough, and Manchester. Eventually he was accepting invitations to lecture in London and Birmingham, and could undertake or research trips not only in Yorkshire but as far away as France and Switzerland. These visits, because of the time it took to travel in a pre-railway age and the need to stay away for several days or even weeks, became a perfect opportunity to meet and correspond with fellow scientists in many different fields.[18]

He also sent frequent written communications on topics of geological and other scientific interest relating to his travels whilst he was away from York to be read out at Society meetings. Many of these reports are kept in the YPS archives.

His role at the Museum involved the maintenance, arrangement and cataloguing of the many diverse collections, and working with the eight Honorary Curators. These were Members who worked in a voluntary capacity in different sections of the Museum, a role that required both considerable scientific knowledge and managerial skills supporting the wider work of the Society. Phillips' close and highly creative relationship with William Vernon was critical to the success of this work.

On November 7th 1826 Phillips' lecture to the Society "*On the probable direction of diluvial currents over parts of Yorkshire*" appeared the following year in the Philosophical Magazine. This was his first scientific publication.[19]

His duties also included receiving distinguished visitors to the Museum, giving him a chance to meet and get to know leading scientists in various fields from other regions of Britain and mainland Europe.These included the pioneering French palaeobotanist Adolphe-Theodore Brogniart (1801–76), the palaeontologist and geologist Gideon Mantell (1790–1852), and the geologist Roderick Impey Murchison (1792–1871).

Murchison was later famed as the first to define the Silurian System for the succession of rocks in the Welsh Borders. In 1855 he was to become Director of the Geological Survey and subsequently awarded a Knighthood in 1863. He was fascinated by the collections in the cramped rooms of the Museum in Low Ousegate. It is recorded that he had to lie on the floor to view certain specimens, but Phillips was able to explain to him crucial facts about the structure of the cliffs of Yorkshire coast which, together with a highly informative boat trip with William Smith along the Whitby cliffs, led to Murchison, in his work in Scotland, to be able to correctly identify the age of the Brora coalfield in Sutherland, Scotland.

The Society had already realised they needed to have adequate purpose-built premises to realise their vision of a great regional museum for the North of England. Three thousand pounds had to be raised by subscription to erect a suitable building on land known as Manor Shore, three acres of semi-derelict land along the banks of the River Ouse, including the ruins of St Mary's Abbey, by the ancient Lendal ferry crossing (the present road bridge was only opened in 1863).

So inspired were the citizens of York that within 10 months of the opening of the subscription in 1825, £4,650 had been raised. After some considerable difficulty and lobbying of Government by Vernon's political friends, the land was acquired, and an architect, William Wilkins, was appointed to design a suitable building in neo-classical Grecian style. In 1827 the foundation stone was laid, appropriately enough, by Vernon's father, the Archbishop of York. Part of the building covered the medieval Abbey's vestibule with the ruins carefully preserved, to this day, in the basement of the Museum among other exhibits.

St Mary's Abbey (author)

St Mary's Lodge – home for many years of John and Anne Phillips (author)

Even before the building was finished, in July 1829, John Phillips was delivering a course of eight lectures there on "aquatic animals" such as water voles and otters.[20] The building finally opened in 1830 to considerable public acclaim, despite the costs having risen, including furniture and fittings, to a massive £9,800. Somehow this money was found. 24,000 exhibits and specimens were transferred under Phillips' supervision from the cramped rooms in Ousegate to be properly displayed in the new Museum.

At the triumphant opening ceremony, attended by both William Smith and John Phillips, amongst the many orations was one from youthful local landowner Sir John Vanden-Bempde Johnstone (1799–1869) of Hackness, Scarborough, who had donated the stone used for the Museum from a quarry on his estate. Johnstone stated that "I cannot look at the Yorkshire Philosophical Society in any other light than the great heart of Science" in the Yorkshire region. There was also warm praise for the new Keeper John Phillips, described by Dr Goldie as "a man of accurate and general science" whose health was duly drunk by all present.[21]

The ambition of the Society was for their Museum to become a major resource and focus for scientific research and study. This ambition went well beyond the confines of display cabinets, and an ever-expanding library. Here would be a fine lecture room, laboratories for research work, a lithograph printer where Phillips could exploit his skill with lithography learned in his teenage years. An observatory was built in the grounds, opened for use in 1833. In many respects, the new Yorkshire Museum fulfilled many of the scientific study and research functions of a modern University, though without the formal structures of students and teaching.

John Phillips played a central role in enabling the Society to realise this vision. He was soon living on site. In 1838 he formally wrote to the Council of the Society[22] requesting permission to lease the somewhat dilapidated late medieval building on the Marygate side of the gardens which had been the Abbey gatehouse. For some years it had housed a run-down ale house – the Brown Cow pub. In return for Phillips' agreement to extensive restoring the building – which he renamed St. Mary's Lodge – the Council generously halved Phillips' own proposals for an annual rent, and only increased it by £10 per annum when the

The restored Hospitium in the Museum Gardens (author)

garden was extensively enlarged to cover almost an acre, continuing down as far as the public Swimming Bath which at that time existed in the corner of the Manor Shore estate.

Interestingly, his sister Anne Phillips (1803–1862) was also made joint lease holder of St Mary's Lodge, no doubt at Phillips' request. Anne had been separated from her brother for some fourteen years, and when they were finally reunited in 1828, she came to live with him at their lodgings in Penley Grove Street in York, as his companion, housekeeper, manager, his emotional support and colleague in science. She was to become a significant figure in geological science in her own right.[23]

For the next fourteen years this small house and carefully landscaped garden (echoing to a degree the larger Museum Garden within which it was contained), were John and Anne Phillips' sanctuary and retreat where they could work, research, write scientific papers and books, and receive guests. In 1850 Phillips even successfully protested about the height of a proposed chimney at the swimming baths immediately below

The Yorkshire Philosophical Society and the Yorkshire Museum

his garden.[24] Though they eventually moved away from York as result of John Phillips' Oxford appointment in 1853, and had subtenants in the Lodge during their longer periods of absence including the period after Anne's death in 1862, John didn't finally surrender the lease until 1870.[25]

The Yorkshire Philosophical Society's vision was also for their Museum Gardens to become more than just a landscape setting for their grand neo-Palladian building, but an extension to the Museum itself, with a clear educational role. Rubbish was cleared, hovels demolished, boatyards and other industrial activities relocated, eyesores removed, trees planted and walkways laid out, and a handsome gateway and porters' lodge was erected. The gifted and energetic Charles Wellbeloved (1769–1858) Unitarian Minister and also Principal of Manchester College (which had agreed to relocate in York in 1803 when Wellbeloved had chosen to move there) was one of the leading campaigners to protect York's historic walls. As Curator of Antiquities (before the term Archaeology became popular), he set about discovering, recording, preserving and collecting Roman and medieval remains from the Museum site and the adjacent St Mary's Abbey ruins, many housed in the eventually restored Hospitium.

Another remarkable figure and close colleague of John Phillips was Henry Baines (1793–1878). Baines was a skilled local gardener, born in a house inside the city walls, who was appointed in 1829 as Sub-Curator, in effect Phillip's right-hand man at a salary of £52 guineas per year.[26] Baines served the Society and the Museum for the next 40 years and had a crucial role in developing and supervising the Gardens, creating a fine botanic garden and later working with landscape gardener Sir John Naesmyth to create much of the public garden that survives today. Baines is also widely remembered for his scholarly **Flora of Yorkshire** published in 1840.

The full, fascinating history of the Museum Gardens is fully told in **The Most Fortunate Situation** by Peter

Henry Baines

Hogarth and Ewan Anderson (YPS 2018). But not everything Phillips, William Vernon Harcourt (as he was now known) and Baines tried was a success. A small menagerie established in 1830 contained a golden eagle, several monkeys and a bear. According to Baines' daughter Fanny, sometime in 1831 *"the bear got loose and chased Professor Phillips and the Rev Vernon Harcourt into an outhouse"*.[27] The menagerie was soon closed and the hapless bear sent to London Zoological gardens on the outside of the regular York to London stagecoach, probably in a cage, accompanied by the long suffering Henry Baines.

The Yorkshire Sections of Smith's 1815 map recreated as a pebble mosaic in the Museum Gardens (author)

The Yorkshire Philosophical Society and the Yorkshire Museum

Such incidents apart, thanks to the inspirational leadership of Phillips and Vernon Harcourt, the Yorkshire Museum and its Gardens became established as one of the leading educational institutes of its day, as well as one of York's top visitor attractions. A visit from the Duchess of Kent and Princess Victoria in 1835 with a gift of £50 and agreement to become patrons gave the Museum and Gardens royal approval.[28] In the early years access was restricted to Members and their friends (and strictly no unsupervised children) but over the years these rules were relaxed with public access at weekend for just one shilling, but there were also regular free open days in the gardens as well as days when Brass Band concerts, flower shows and other events took place. In 1844 a train 26 carriages long brought a party of over a thousand schoolchildren from industrial Wakefield to York to visit the Museum and the Gardens.[29] In 1845 alone, it was estimated that between two and three thousand "railway excursionists" had visited the gardens and museum at specially reduced rates.[30]

The reputation of the Yorkshire Museum and its Gardens was now secure.

Today as it approaches its bicentenary, the Yorkshire Philosophical Society continues to be a lively focal point and meeting for amateur and professional natural scientists and historians throughout the region. Only a few years younger, the Yorkshire Museum is as relevant for people of the twenty-first century as it was for those of the nineteenth and the twentieth. It has become one of the great Museums of the North of England, with collections that are of international importance, specialising, as it always has, in both the natural sciences and archaeology. Still to be seen are some of the original Kirkdale Cave remains, as well as many of the original Roman and medieval artefacts from the Abbey ruins and from other sites in York that Charles Wellbeloved and others collected. But there is much more besides. Of course the latest techniques of interpretation and presentation have long overtaken the traditional static exhibits in glass cases, and fittingly, it is the Jurassic heritage of the Yorkshire Coast – an area of Yorkshire so eloquently described by John Phillips in his **Illustrations of the Geology of Yorkshire** – which is still frequently used to capture the imagination of younger audiences as the Age of the Dinosaurs.

It is also worth visitors wandering up to the second floor to peer into what is currently the Reading Room. At time of writing this space contains the Museum Library which holds part of the Philosophical Society's original book collections and retains much of the atmosphere of the Phillips/Harcourt era. As well as an actual (1824) version of William Smith's 1815 Geological Map on display and other memorabilia of the Heroic Age of Geology, you'll find portraits of both Smith and Phillips still presiding over the institution that so reflected and helped to deliver their vision.

Also not to be missed on a visit to the Yorkshire Museum Gardens is the fine reinterpretation of the Yorkshire Section of Smith's pioneering England & Wales Map, recreated as a walk-on mosaic pebble map in the Museum Gardens, close to the ruins of St Mary's Abbey near the pavilion of the former bowling green. Commissioned jointly by the Yorkshire Philosophical Society and the Yorkshire Museums Trust in 2015, it was created by artist Janette Ireland using coloured pebbles, actual fossils, discarded stone from the Minster and tiny tesserae, using colours that reflect those used in the original map, an imaginative tribute to the pioneering work of Smith and Phillips, geological map makers extraordinary.

Yorkshire
Philosophical
Society

Notes

1 Phillips John 1844: *Memoirs of William Smith* London: John Murray p103

2 *Ibid.* p104

3 *Ibid.* p107

4 Edmonds J.M. 1975 *The Geological Lecture Courses given in Yorkshire by William Smith and John Phillips 1824–25* Proc of Yorkshire Geological Society 40(3) p373–412

5 Akehurst A. M. 2009 *The very best of its kind out of the Metropolis: The Foundation of Yorkshire Philosophical Society, the Yorkshire Museum and its Gardens in the early Nineteenth Century* York ac.uk.

6 Buckland William 1822 *Reliquiae Diluvianae; or Observations on the Organic remains contained in Caves, Fissures and Diluvial Gravel and on other Geological Phenomena attesting to the Action of an Universal Deluge.* London: John Murray.

7 Orange A.D. 1973 Philosophers and Provincials: *The Yorkshire Philosophical Society from 1822–1844* York: YPS p11

8 Pyrah BJ 1988 *The History of the Yorkshire Museum* York: Sessions pp22–24

9 Chapman, Allen 2001 *The Grand Amateur Tradition of Science in Victorian England.* in *Yorkshire People and Places* York: YPS

10 Rubinstein David 2009 *The Nature of the World: Yorkshire Philosophical Society 1822–2000.* York: YPS p5

11 Rubinstein David 2009 *ibid.* p6

12 Orange A.D. 1973 *op. cit.* p23–25

13 Phillips John 1844 *op. cit.* p107

14 Phillips John 1844 *ibid.* p109

15 Phillips John: 1865 *The Rivers Mountains and Sea Coast of Yorkshire.* London: Murray p72

16 Minutes of the Yorkshire Philosophical Society Council – 11th November 1825

17 Yorkshire Philosophical Society 1825 – Annual Report for 1824 p5

18 Pyrah BJ 1988 op. cit p38

19 Annual Report of the Council of the Yorkshire Philosophical Society 1875 p14

20 Orange A.D. 1973 *op. cit.* p29

21 Yorkshire Gazette, 6th February 1830

22 Minutes of YPS Council meeting 1st October 1838

23 Morgan Nina 2007 *Anne Phillips: John Phillips' Geological Companion* Geological Society, London Special Publication 281 pp265–275

24 Rubinstein 2009 Op. Cit p24

25 Hogarth P.J, & Anderson E.W. 2018 *The Most Fortunate Situation: The story of Yorkshire Museum's Gardens* York: YPS pp64–66

26 Morrell Jack 2005 *John Phillips and the Victorian Business of Science* Aldershot: Ashgate p119

27 Hogarth P.J, & Anderson E.W. 2018 *op. cit.* pp84–5

28 Morrell Jack 2005 *op. cit.* p156

29 Hogarth P.J, & Anderson E.W. 2018 *op. cit.* pp141–2

30 Rubinstein David 2009 *op. cit.* p20

Cayton Bay looking northwards towards Osgodby Point, a geologically complex headland formed by Middle Jurassic limestones of the Millepore Bed faulted against sandstones of the Osgodby Formation, capped by glacial Boulder Clay (Andy Howard)

3

Yorkshire's Coast, Wolds and Moors

In the summer of 1824, after his successful first series of York lectures, and in order to raise some badly needed extra income, William Smith decided to give a course of lectures in Scarborough. John once again assisted his uncle, no doubt bringing order to Smith's somewhat chaotic deliberations, as well as contributing three lectures of the series on organic fossils. Scarborough's Rotunda Museum has a copy on display of the "Syllabus" of this course of lectures at the old Town Hall. The lectures took place every Monday, Wednesday and Friday at 1pm, over a three-week period costing a guinea for whole course of lectures or 3 shillings per individual lecture – even that quite a percentage of an average week's wages for an ordinary working man or woman. People attended the lectures not just from Scarborough, but from areas much further away, many of the audience happy to combine a visit to Scarborough's spa with a learned lecture.

Smith and Phillips already had a good relationship with the local scientific community, dating from their visits in 1820 and afterwards, during their geological wanderings and survey work in the area. These had included meeting local fossil collectors, botanists and gentlemen scientists in the town. Following the success of the Scarborough lectures, Smith was soon engaged to deliver a course of lectures to the Literary and Philosophical Societies of both Hull and Sheffield. After the Hull series, Smith and Phillips returned to examine the complex strata around Castle Hill, Scarborough. This was to become a significant location for John Phillips. As he was to write in a letter to Smith in 1825 *Scarborough Castle is surely the finest spot for a Geologist that the whole earth contains*.[1]

SYLLABUS

OF

LECTURES ON GEOLOGY

IN THE

Town-Hall, Scarborough,

BY

W. SMITH,

Author of the Geological Map of England and Wales, Geological
Map of Yorkshire and other Counties, &c. &c. Honorary Member
of the Yorkshire and Bristol Philosophical Societies, &c.

Including three Lectures on Organic Fossils by his nephew

J. PHILLIPS,

Honorary Member of the Yorkshire Philosophical Society.

*The Lectures will be given every Monday, Wednesday,
and Friday, at one o'clock,*

viz.

Lect. 1. Monday, August... 30.	Lect. 6. Friday ....10th. Sept.
2. Wednesday 1st. Sept.	7. Monday ....13th. Sept.
3. Friday.. ,...3rd. Sept.	8. Wednesday 15th. Sept.
4. Monday.....6th. Sept	9. Friday ......17th. Sept.
5. Wednesday 8th. Sept.	

Tickets may be obtained of Mr. Cole, Newborough, Mr,
Brooks, Cliff, and Mr. Wilson, Long-Room Street.

Admission ticket for the course (transferable) £1 1 0
*Ditto for a Single Lecture.... ....*0 3 0

But as they were completing their survey work around Scarborough's
cliffs, William Smith suffered what was described as a rheumatic attack
which made it difficult for him to stand or walk. His Sheffield lectures
had to be delivered from a sitting position.[2] Although he did recover from
the condition, from that time Smith was happy to hand over most of the
lecturing to his eloquent nephew.

In 1826 Smith, no doubt with the encouragement of his Scarborough
friends, came to live permanently in Scarborough, the town's cleaner air

good for his own health and that of his ailing wife Mary Ann. It was also a useful base for Smith and Phillips from where to undertake their own survey work along the whole of the coast. They were soon examining and giving advice on local fossil collections which were to form the basis of the first collections of the Scarborough Philosophical Society to be housed in their proposed Museum.

One of these fossil collecting enthusiasts, a local doctor John Dunn (1790–1851), *"one of the most affectionate and highly esteemed of (Smith's) friends"*, later became the first Secretary of the Scarborough Philosophical Society when it was founded in 1827. Others who were to become close friends of both Smith and Phillips included John Williamson (1784–1877) later first Keeper of the Scarborough Museum, with whom Smith lodged for some time, and his cousin William Bean, (1787–1866) another keen palaeontologist, conchologist and collector.

Phillips noted[3] how much his uncle enjoyed the dramatic cliff landscape of both Scarborough and Whitby. The two geologists took long coastal walks together, observing the contrasting impacts of tide and wave erosion on the different rock structures along the coast. They were soon examining the rocks and collecting fossils around Speeton and Grisethorpe further to the south. Smith produced new papers on local geology, and modified his Yorkshire map in the light of new research to also prepare what would be his geological map of Scarborough.

Scarborough Castle viewed from North Bay. The precipitous slopes of Castle Hill are formed by the Oxford Clay Formation, capped by resistant sandstones and limestones of the Corallian (Andy Howard)

Sir John Johnstone

Through the network of his friends and admirers, and no doubt including the energetic efforts both of his nephew and of Vernon Harcourt, in 1828 William was appointed land steward for the estate of Sir John Johnstone, by then President of the Scarborough Philosophical Society and keen amateur scientist in his own right. The estate at Hackness was about seven miles west of Scarborough. With Mary Ann now sadly in an asylum, Smith could at least enjoy a period of pleasant, permanent employment on a country estate. His reputation as one of England's greatest scientific figures was now secured. In 1831, the Geological Society, finally repenting of their earlier neglect, awarded him their first prestigious Wollaston Medal for his services to the science and with it a modest but badly needed pension. This, together with the salary from Sir John Johnstone, could finally give the elderly geologist the financial security that had eluded him all his life. In 1831, encouraged by Johnstone, Smith produced his geological map of Scarborough and its surrounds,[4] and in 1832, his final map, appropriately the *Stratification of the Hackness Hills*. 1834 he finally retired, moving into Newburgh Cottage in Bar Street in the centre of the town with a modest pension of £20 from the generous Johnstone *"for occasional advice and visits"*.

But for John Phillips 1826 was the beginning of a new career as a peripatetic lecturer and teacher, which had started at first with his uncle, but soon was undertaken totally independently. The best option for a young lecturer was to be hired by a learned society at an agreed fee for a whole series of lectures, but on some occasions the lecturer simply kept the lecture fees paid by the students less the cost of the room. This could prove precarious if, because of bad weather or local apathy, turnout was poor. But Phillips was soon in constant demand, as a well informed and entertaining lecturer, not only in York and Scarborough, but as far away as Hull, Leeds, Sheffield and Manchester.

There was also still time between these demanding commitments, for Phillips to further his own geological and palaeontological knowledge through detailed field work, squeezing the work in between his curatorial and lecturing commitments. In the autumn of 1828, following a walk he had originally undertaken in 1824 between York and Scarborough via Helmsley and Kirkbymoorside, and further survey work he had undertaken with friends in 1826 and 1827, Phillips published a detailed survey of the geology of the northern slopes of the Vale of Pickering,[5] the southern edge of what is now the North York Moors National Park. He even noted errors in Buckland's estimate of the height of Kirkdale Cave above the valley floor. But Phillips was able to confirm from fossil evidence the similarities of the strata in the North Riding of Yorkshire to those in southern England – Oxfordshire (Oxford Clay) and Dorset (Kimmeridge Clay) – and prove also the continuity of the identical strata observed at the coast inland and into the high moorland areas.

In 1829, with his friends William Vernon and John Salmond, Phillips undertook an investigation at Bielsbeck, two miles south of Market Weighton, on the edge of the Yorkshire Wolds, where in a local marl pit a quantity of important fossil mammal bones was uncovered, including elephant, rhinoceros, lion, reindeer, horse, wolf and bison bones, again offering an insight into the fauna of "pre-diluvial" Yorkshire.[6] The finds caused some tension between the Yorkshire and Hull Museums, the Hull curator protesting that the best specimens, on the orders of the landowner, William Worsley of Hovingham, had been given to York even though they were found in East Yorkshire.[7]

A Yorkshire Lion: lion jawbones excavated at Bieslbeck Quarry, near Market Weighton (Yorkshire Museum Collection: Specimen YORM:YM699)

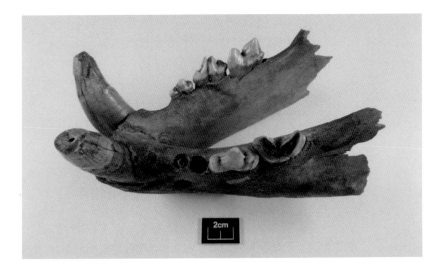

Despite all this intense activity linked to the Society and his curatorial duties at the Museum, his lectures and research trips, John Phillips also found time to write and self-publish in 1829 his first major scientific work, the **Illustrations of The Geology of Yorkshire or Description of the Strata and organic remains of the Yorkshire Coast.** This was a project that the YPS encouraged and perceived as one that reflected their core objects. It was a ground-breaking publication by their Museum Keeper and Secretary that would also bring a great deal of prestige and credit to the Society.

It was written in a few weeks between November 1828 and February 1829. It synthesised much of Phillip's recent lecture material and the new survey work he had done in 1827 and 1828 along the coast. The book also replaced relatively inadequate – if pioneering – coastal sections by Scriptural Geologist Reverend George Young and local artist John Bird, and even studies by Professor Adam Sedgwick, who was quick to congratulate Phillips on the work. Phillips also had concerns about competition from a rival Thomas Webster who surveying the coast at that time and was planning a publication.

Rotunda Museum, Scarborough (author)

Yorkshire's Coast, Wolds and Moors

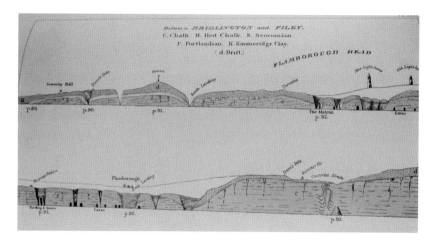

Geological sections of Flamborough Head by John Phillips from **Illustrations of the Geology of Yorkshire** (collection Yorkshire Museum)

Dedicated to his uncle William Smith, self-published, but financed by pre-publication public subscriptions at £1 per copy, and printed by Thomas Wilson of York, the essence of the book came through a coloured map, and detailed section diagrams of 100 miles of the coast at a scale of 1½ inches to the mile, a vertical section at one inch to 400 feet. This was measured with great accuracy with Phillips' own mountain barometer. There were also 14 detailed lithographed plates of fossil specimens typical to the area. All were drawn by Phillips himself and lithographed by T.Ingbold of Leeds. Some of the specimens he used for the drawings are now in the Whitby Museum.

It was an immediate bestseller. As well as 400 pre-paying subscribers, it was soon on sale in bookshops via the publishers John Murray in London. The book won praise from leading figures in science. It rapidly established John Phillips as one of the most brilliant field geologists of his generation. Given the wealth of detailed scientific information, research and scholarship in its 200 or so pages, the book was a *tour de force* for a 28-year-old, who had received no formal higher education.

To understand what the book is about, it is worth making a visit to one of Yorkshire's most remarkable Museums, the former Scarborough City Museum, now known as The Rotunda – the William Smith Museum of Geology. Opened in August 1829, this handsome Doric temple-like building, in a side valley close to the seafront, was built by the Scarborough Philosophical Society to a design by Richard Hey Sharp of York but following suggestions made by William Smith. It was Britain's, and one of the world's, first purpose-built science museums. The two wings were added to extend the display areas in 1860.

As John Dunn records:

> *The circular plan of the building was originally suggested by*
> *Mr Smith, as being capable of exhibiting in a simple, intelligible*
> *form the stratifications of the rocks of Great Britain on sloping*
> *shelves according to their stratigraphical order, the study of the*
> *once intricate science of geology would then be reduced to the*
> *greatest degree of simplicity.*[8]

The theory was simple – to create a spiral diorama using John Phillips'
geological sections of the Yorkshire coastline with the actual fossils
displayed in their correct stratigraphical order on the sloping shelves

The SPS Minute book contains detailed lists of the costs of the work on
the building, including a fee of over £50 to *"Mr Smith"* for preparing the
ground (a not insignificant sum but which would have included payment
for supervising some major civil engineering and drainage works on
steeply sloping land). The SPS Council Minutes of March 30 noted that
it was resolved *"that Mr Todd be engaged to paint a geological section of the*
strata of the coast in oil colours" for a fee of £3. This must have included the
demanding task of transcribing and painting Phillips' complex geological
sections onto the frieze. Sadly it turned out later that the shelves had
been installed the wrong way and the frieze painted to mirror the slope,
so that when restored in 1906 it had to be reversed.

After some years of neglect, in 2008 The Rotunda Museum was
brilliantly and imaginatively restored and re-branded as the William
Smith Museum of Geology, with Phillips' frieze superbly recreated, using
his colour coding of strata and their fossils. In addition are fascinating
displays of relevant fossils in their correct stratigraphical order These
include many fine specimens collected by early members of the Society
locally, as well as material from William Smith's original fossil collection
that he had been forced to sell to the British Museum in 1812 and some
of the original fossils found at Kirkdale Cave. There are also maps,
including a three-quarter sized copy of Smith's famous map of England
and Wales, and a replica of his Hackness map, memorabilia and portraits
of Smith, Phillips and other major local scientific figures, involved with
the development of the Scarborough Philosophical Society or local
scientific discoveries. These include Sir John Johnstone who donated

£100 towards the cost of building of the Rotunda as well as providing the stone – Kellaway rock – from his estate. Another supporter was the aeronautical pioneer Sir George Cayley, (1773–1857) who is featured as a friend and correspondent of William Smith. The Museum is also the starting point of The William Smith Trail, a walk around the town, taking in the Old Town Hall, where Smith and Phillips gave pioneering lectures, and Chapman's Yard, site of the Town Reservoir built by Smith. The Trail focuses on Phillips' favourite Castle Hill.

Illustrations of The Geology of Yorkshire is also a fine piece of scientific literature in its own right. Like so many major scientific figures of the nineteenth century, Phillips had an enviable command of the English language and could write clear, concise prose.

After an Introduction that describes his work in Yorkshire, the first part of the book presents an extended essay on Geology as a pragmatic and empirical science, as understood at that time. This section is very much based on the work of contemporary leading figures of geology and palaeontology, figures such as Werner, Hutton, Lyell, and Cuvier and above all Smith himself, whom Phillips praises above all for the empirical and practical nature of his research.

But for a modern reader, despite Phillips' grasp of the epic nature of the many complex processes that have shaped the planet, a difficulty remains in the almost universally held concept at that time that even though Genesis for most progressive Christians was understood to be not literally true, but a metaphor of the whole long process of Creation, there was still a firm belief among scientists that there had been one huge single Biblical Flood that had shaped the world we now see. Fossils are frequently described as being "antediluvian" or "postdiluvian" as a major – literal – watershed in the earth's history. What we would now call glacial deposits are often described as diluvial, even if they are clearly not water-transported deposits. What we see in the eroded and sculptured landscape of the Dales, Moors and to some extent Wolds we now perceive as being largely caused by glaciation, and not just floods. It was not until the 1840s and indeed decades later following the great work on Alpine glaciers by JRL Agassiz (1817–73) that, what to later generations seem glaringly obvious, became widely accepted.[9] It took even longer for there to be recognition that there was not one single Ice Age but several glacial episodes, the last one only ending some 12,000 years ago.

Significantly, Phillips concludes his opening chapter with the kind of grand rhetoric no modern geologist would dare risk, an assertion that the great purpose of science is for mankind to understand the purposes of the Almighty. But He was a God nevertheless who stays quietly in the background, which even an agnostic twenty-first century reader, who might substitute the word "Nature" as the final word in the text, could find meaningful:

> *This transient flood retired from the desolated continent: again the forest is clothed with foliage; birds fly in the air, and animals roam the earth; the mountains gather clouds, rain falls, the streams flow down their new channels, the sea resumes its appointed boundary; cliffs are wasted, low shores are extended, vallies (sic) fill up, volcanoes are in action; nature revives again, and man, by contemplation of the phenomena, reads the awful history of his birthplace, gathers ideas of the immense agency entered in the construction of the earth, compares this planet with the other members of the solar system, and views the solar system itself as only a small part of the immeasurable works of God!*[10]

From Chapter Two onwards another aspect of Phillips is revealed – the topographer, the writer who can capture in relatively few words the essence of a landscape; not, as contemporary topographers usually did in flowery language and vague generalisations, but with an exactness of description and sharpness of detail. It is difficult even two centuries later to better the opening description of the topography of Yorkshire: *"one of the few counties in England which are, for the most part, defined by natural boundaries"*.

Phillips describes how the west of the county includes what we now call the Yorkshire Dales and the Pennines, the east the Yorkshire Wolds and North York Moors, divided through the centre of the lowland Vale of York.

> *a broad, level vale … filled with gravel deposited on the red sandstone …*

from beneath which:

> *rises towards the west an elevated undulated tract of carboniferous and calcareous rocks which ascend to the summit*

*of Micklefell, Ingleborough and Pendle hill; whilst above, on
the east, appear the uniformities of the chalk and oolite. The
hilly western tract is grouped in two portions: the district south
of the Aire, in which generally, sandstones and shales with coal
abound; and the more elevated region north of that river whose
romantic dales are sunk into mountain limestone, and whose
hills are capped by the lower members of the coal series.[11]*

The eastern part of Yorkshire – the main focus of the book – he
categorises into five subdivisions. These consists of the two great,
scenically beautiful areas of moorland and coast, consisting of the
Jurassic series of sandstones, shales and limestones, penetrated by
deep river valleys, an area that we now know as the North York Moors
National Park. This comprises of what he described as **The Moorland
District** – the Cleveland Hills and great escarpment overlooking the
Vale of Cleveland and extending eastwards as far as the great line of cliffs
between Redcar and Scarborough, and to its south **The Tabular Oolitic
Hills** (The term "Tabular Hills" was first used by Phillips) extending
from Hambleton and Sutton Bank in the west and running, north of
the Vale of Pickering to the coast between Scarborough and Filey again
penetrated by narrow river valleys:

Lake Gormire and Sutton Bank on the edge of the Tabular Hills (Walking Englishman)

*These hills meet the sea-coast between Filey and Scarborough
on the east. They rise toward the north from under the vale of
Pickering, and terminate in a remarkable line of escarpments
at Sipho Brow, Blakehoe Topping, Saltergate, Lestingham,
Easterside and Black Hambleton. From the Vale of Pickering
the ascent is long and gradual, but from the northern moors
is very short and abrupt. The altitude of the hills increases
westward. Thus, Gristhorpe cliffs are about two hundred and
seventy feet high; Oliver's Mount, four hundred and ninety
feet; the heights above Troutbeck, six hundred and fifty feet;
above Rievaulx Abbey eight hundred feet; at Hambleton, twelve
hundred and forty-six feet. Even at considerable distance, the
plane summits and abrupt terminations of these oolitic hills are
very remarkable.*[12]

Then follows his description of the **Vale of Pickering** that he correctly
suggests was once a great lake, followed by a brief section on **The Chalk
Wolds** and more extended section on **Holderness** and its rich organic
fossil remains.

Horsedale near Huggate in the Yorkshire Wolds, a characteristic grass-bottomed,
dry chalk valley (author)

Spurn Head looking southwards from Kilnsea. Photographed in September 2018, the image shows extensive erosion of the beach by the Beast from the East storm of the preceding spring (Andy Howard)

Phillips follows this account with a table, illustrating the series of strata from the newer Cretaceous rocks of White Chalk that comprise the Wolds, down to the yet at that time to be explored ancient slates around Ingleton and Sedbergh in the north west of Yorkshire.

But this first volume of the **Illustrations** is primarily concerned with the east. Phillips suggests an image of the geological structure of the earth being like a gigantic layered cake. Using Smithian insights into the angles of dips and slopes of the strata, he suggests how the coastal cliffs give a clear overview and insight into the structure of the layers that continue inland. Supplemented by countless observations in quarries, cuttings and outcrops, the coastal cliffs for Phillips were the key to an understanding of the whole of eastern Yorkshire.

Phillips notes the many similarities between what we now know as the Jurassic rocks of the Cleveland Hills with those of the edge of the Cotswolds in Gloucestershire[13] and proceeds to give a detailed analysis of the huge area of sandstones, ironstones and shales which continue under the eastern side of Yorkshire, beneath the Vale of Pickering and the distinctive, newer chalk uplands of the Wolds.

His description of the Yorkshire Wolds offers a concise word-picture:

> "High and bare of trees, yet not dreary nor sterile, they are
> furrowed as all other chalk-hills by smooth winding, ramified

vallies (sic), without any channel for a stream. Where several of these vallies meet, they produce a very pleasing combination of salient and retiring slopes, which resemble, on a grand scale, the petty concavities and projections in the actual channel of a river. Doubtless these vallies were excavated by water, but not the water of rains or springs or rivulets. Some greater flood, in more ancient times, has performed the work, and left the traces of its extent on the pebbles which it has deposited along its course."[14]

The "greater flood" of course as we now know were several periods of glacial activity, together with interglacial, freeze-thaw conditions creating temporary, fast flowing, highly erosive streams, cutting their way through the soft chalk to create the present distinctive dry valleys.[15]

Phillips now gives his attention to the coast starting at Holderness.

From Spurn Point, the most southerly tip of Holderness, the reader is given an evocative description of the constant erosive action of the sea:

"the whole shore is in motion, every cliff is hastening to its fall, the parishes are contracted, the churches washed away, and reasonable fears are entertained that at some time the water of the ocean and the Humber may join, and the Spurn became an island."[16]

That duly happened in 2013 when a huge tidal surge washed away the road to the lighthouse and Spurn Point officially became a "tidal island".

From Spurn Point the reader is taken north along the coast, with descriptions of key features and of major fossil discoveries along the shore, such as the remains of the extinct Great Elk, found by an old man collecting gravel at Skirlington between Hornsea and Skipsea. There is a fine description of Flamborough Head which combines the enthusiasm of the topographer with the drier observations of the geologist – as Phillips suggests the caves at North Landing in the depressed chalk are *"worthy of examination by the lover of scenery and the geologist"*. There follow some fascinating observations of how the caves and other features were created by the action of the tide, how the cliffs on the northern and southern

The dramatic chalk cliffs and sea-carved inlets of Flamborough Head, Yorkshire Wolds (Dorian Speakman)

sides of Flamborough Head differ in appearance because of the action of the waves, and how the upper strata between Bridlington and South Landing are rich in fossils, but the lower levels in contrast far less so. He also notes that the chalk of East Yorkshire is far poorer in fossil remains than other chalk areas of England.

Phillips then follows the coastline to Scarborough. He describes a walk in some detail between White Nab and Scarborough Spa and explains the significance of what can be observed along and below the cliff face.

This section of the book ends at what for Phillips is the jewel in the crown – Scarborough's distinctive Castle Hill, whose complex geological structure is analysed in a masterly way.

The rest of the coast northwards to Robin Hoods Bay and Whitby is detailed in the same precise way with reference to the characteristic fossils to be seen, embedded in the rock, including remains of mammoths. It was left to later generations to identify the gigantic dinosaur footprints printed in sand or mud, petrified to sandstone or mudstones, that have given this section of the coast the soubriquet *The Dinosaur Coast*.

A view across Robin Hood's Bay from Dungeon Hole The seaweed-covered wave cut platform is formed by grey mudstone of the Redcar Mudstone Formation. The Ferruginous Sandstone boulder in the foreground is a remnant of a rockfall (possibly some centuries ago) from beds of Staithes Sandstone high in the cliff (Dorian Speakman)

Phillips also describes in some detail, the major dislocation or fault line which extends along the valley of the River Esk upstream from Whitby, creating low cliffs.

But as the Whitby geologist and author Roger Osborne notes[17] Phillips – taking his cue from earlier work by Rev George Young – had made a significant over-estimation of the scale of this fault, an error only rectified over 150 years later by Professor Hemingway and others equipped with new methods of analysing river delta deposits.

Phillips goes on explore the coast beyond Sandsend. He describes in detail the area around the alum works at Lyth and Kettleness, continuing to Runswick Bay, noting what at that time was believed to be another great dislocation of the strata around the little creek and harbour at Staithes, whose high cliffs, together with those at Boulby, he analyses with listings of minerals and fossils.

In a section on what he calls The Diluvium – which we would now describe as Glacial Till – Phillips reflects on the rich variety of minerals and boulders and pebbles, and even mammoth bones, brought from as far away as Teesdale, Cumberland and even Scotland, he assumes by the action of water.

The last part of **Illustrations**, apart from a short chapter on the practical and commercial use of local stone and minerals, (including typical building stone), and iron, coal and alum mines, is devoted to a detailed listing and description of the rich variety of characteristic fossils to be found along the Yorkshire coast. The section begins with a wide-ranging essay on how the chemical composition of animals and plants change during the long process of fossilisation, and how the different geological areas of Yorkshire reveal totally different species:

As he notes:

> *The mountain limestone of the north-western dales of*
> *Yorkshire abounds with crinoidea, productae, spiriferae, and*
> *bellerphontes, of which no single individual has ever been*
> *found in the eastern part of the county, which on the other*
> *hand, contain echini, trigoniae, cucullaeae, rostellarieae, and*
> *ammonites, to which there is nothing similar in the west.*[18]

View of the quay and Cowbar Nab at Staithes taken in 1897 by W.J. Harrison. Note the lady on the quayside waring a traditional Staithes bonnet (British Geological Survey Geoscenic Collection)

Phillips also suggests how it is possible to apply zoological principles to ascertain the nature of the species or subspecies of fossil and thereby establishing the precise order of sequence of strata in which they have been discovered relative to other strata. This therefore is a key indicator to the age and to rocks and strata – not just in England but as he notes in other countries of Europe and the world. He also gives a useful summary of the Kirkdale Cave discoveries.

The book concludes with tables and lists of the rich variety of plant and animal fossils and where they are to be found in the east of Yorkshire, illustrated by the series of 14 Plates, all detailed engraved drawings of typical fossils, each linked to their appropriate stratum.

In many ways, **Illustrations of the Geology of Yorkshire** is a tribute to William Smith that goes far beyond the fulsome dedication. It is a skilful articulation and expansion of the principles of stratigraphy and palaeontology Smith had taught his nephew, applied to the Yorkshire Coast. As Phillips concludes:

> *These researches, commenced by Mr Smith in England, have extended with the same results over all parts of Europe, and a large portion of America, and therefore it is concluded that strata, or groups of strata, are to be discriminated in local regions and identified in distant countries, by their imbedded organic remains.*[19]

Or put another way: William Smith was not just the Father of English Geology. He was a Founder of Stratigraphy on a world scale and John Phillips' treatise on the Yorkshire Coast was a celebration of that fact.

Notes

1   Phillips J letter to William Smith 12.4.25 quoted in YPS Scientific Communications (York University Borthwick Library Archive)

2   Phillips John 1844 *Memoirs of William Smith* London: John Murray p111

3   Phillips John 1844 *ibid.*

4   Geological Society: www.geolsoc.org.uk/Library-and-Information-Services/Exhibitions/William-Strata-Smith/Final-years/Map-of-Scarborough

5   Phillips J 1828 *Remarks on the Geology of the North Side of the Vale of Pickering in Transactions of the Philosophical Society* XL

6   Vernon W.V. *On a discovery of Fossil Bones in a Marl Pit near North Cliffe*. Philosophical Magazine XX1 p225–31

7   Sheppard T. 1933 Proceedings of the Yorkshire Geological Society vol 22 pp169–177

8   First Report of the Scarborough Philosophical Society 1830

9   Robson Douglas A. *1986 Pioneers of Geology* – Hancock Museum, Newcastle p39–40

10 Phillips John 1829 *Illustrations of the Geology of Yorkshire or a Description of the Strata and Organic Remains of the Yorkshire Coast* York: author pp29–30

11 *Ibid.* p31

12 *Ibid.* p43

13 *Ibid.* p34

14 *Ibid.* p46

15 Gobbet D. and Myerscough R, 2018 *Geology and Landscape in The Yorkshire Wolds Landscape – Past, Present and Future* York: Place pp10–14

16 Phillips John 1929 Op. Cit p60

17 Osborne Roger 1998 *The Floating Egg* London: Jonathan Cape pp266–286

18 Phillips John 1829 *op. cit.* p115

19 *Ibid.* p115

York from the historic city walls (Dorian Speakman)

4

The British Association in York

John Phillips' **Illustrations of the Geology of Yorkshire – the Yorkshire Coast** rapidly established his reputation as one of the most gifted young scientists of his generation.

From 1826 York had become his home, both physically and spiritually. His work was now highly valued by the Yorkshire Philosophical Society, especially by his friend William Vernon Harcourt, as he was known, on adopting his father's new surname. Harcourt was the Society's President until 1831 (Lord Milton assuming the nominal title of President in that year) but continued, in his capacity as Vice President, to be the leading moving force of the Society. As well as being an extremely knowledgeable scientific figure in his own right, Harcourt was an able administrator and shrewd political operator – and close ally of John Phillips.

The relationship between Harcourt and Phillips was to prove a dynamic and creative partnership. Keen to ensure his young protégé stayed in York, in 1831 Harcourt secured a much-needed increase in salary for Phillips, now both Museum Keeper and Society Secretary, to £100 per annum, which with additional earnings from lecturing gave Phillips the financial security which had until then eluded him. He was even able to help William Smith with a £10 gift during one of his uncle's periods of financial distress.

The Yorkshire Philosophical Society under the direction of liberal minded, Broad Church Anglicans such as Harcourt and Phillips also opened their doors and worked closely with other religions denominations, most notably Dissenters such as Methodists, Unitarians, Baptists and Quakers. Men such as Unitarians Charles Wellbeloved and John Kenrick and leading local Quakers Thomas Backhouse and William Hinks all continued to be close friends of Phillips.

Phillips was soon persuaded to give lectures, without receiving a fee, to the York Mechanics Institute, founded in 1827 to give working men an opportunity for self-improvement by offering lectures and tuition in a variety of subjects. The Institute had created a library and reading room open to the public for further study and research.

At the banquet to celebrate the opening of the Yorkshire Museum in 1830, Wellbeloved spoke movingly of the value of the library of the Institute to at least some ordinary working people:

> *I will tell you what I have seen. I have seen a number of young persons come, night after night, to the library to carry home books to read by their firesides, and to lead them out of improper courses which they would (otherwise) fall into ...*[1]

Education was about empowerment – but also about moral improvement. Wellbeloved had even given 89 of his own personal books to the Institute Library.[2]

By 1834 John Phillips was giving a series of lectures to the Institute on palaeontology, physical geography, coal mining and meteorology. These were all given by him without a fee in order to encourage a wider interest in the natural sciences – linked to personal improvement – among the wider population and lower classes of York.

Charles Wellbeloved

Sadly, the York Mechanics Institute, didn't quite attract all the working mechanics its founders had envisaged. This was a time of industrial decline and apathy before the arrival of the railways and subsequent growth of manufacturing in the 1840s. In 1838 the Institute was relaunched as the York Institute of Popular Science and Literature to attract a wider audience of lower middle-class trades people, such as clerks, shopkeepers and teachers – an evolution not unlike that of the Workers Educational Association of the twentieth century. Women could also attend.

Phillips did not confine his lectures to scientific societies and Mechanics Institutes to geology and palaeontology. He was eloquent on topics within the sister sciences of zoology and botany, cross referencing between these and other disciplines such as chemistry, physics, and astronomy, to a point where his range of interests and knowledge were described by John Dunn, Secretary of the Scarborough Philosophical Society, as the product of a highly gifted *cyclopaedia of science*.[3] By his 30s Phillips was a remarkable polymath, though perhaps it should be remembered that many sciences, still in their infancy, were far easier to access in depth by an intelligent, literate individual in the 1830s than they would be to a layperson in the twenty-first century, even within a single discipline.

The historian David Elliston Allen has described in some detail the way in which Romantic and Evangelical values in Regency and early Victorian times led to a huge interest and involvement in natural history, most especially geology, botany and ornithology, with an obsession for classification and categorisation.[4] Phillips was both a part of this culture and a major contributor to it.

In 1830 Phillips even initiated a series of free public lectures at the Museum during the York Assizes designed to be available to all the people of York. It was reported in the local press that "belles of the ballroom" as well as "sages of the assizes" attended the lectures[5] – a reference to women being able to attend these academic gatherings.

As the American science writer Michon Scott has argued:

> *Phillips used his insider power to open up scientific meetings to women. His acknowledgement of female ability was likely*

influenced by his sister Anne. Neither John nor Anne ever married, and she served as his housekeeper for over 30 years, until she died in 1862. But the help she gave him was more than domestic; she contributed to his geological work, too, even finding a conglomerate supporting his hypothesis about the formation of the Malvern Hills.[6]

There was not at that time the hard division between professional and amateur scientists which has since developed in many scientific disciplines – areas such as botany and ornithology being perhaps notable exceptions. Many enthusiastic amateurs collecting fossils or plants in the first part of the nineteenth century could work on an equal level to the professor or university researcher. Phillips would always speak to these local amateurs in his work around the whole of the British Isles, sharing their knowledge and in some case even their specimens or research findings. But in every case their work and research were always fully acknowledged. Phillip's major contribution was in seeing the bigger picture and fitting local discoveries into a wider national and international context.

Many of these people might not be able to pay the cost of a series of Philosophical Society lectures or even an individual lecture to mingle with well-dressed ladies and gentlemen, but could go along to an inspiring talk with other working people by someone of the calibre of John Phillips, at their local Mechanics Institute.

By the early 1830s, John Phillips was taking up speaking engagements at leading Philosophical Societies and Mechanics Institutes on both sides of the Pennines, Leeds, Manchester, and even London. Though the building of new and ever improving turnpike roads with fast stagecoach and even overnight mail coach services had dramatically reduced

Mail coach to London about to depart from the Swan Inn 1830s (from Tom Bradley, **The Old Coaching days in Yorkshire 1889**)

travel times, steam railways that were to revolutionise travel and the spread of knowledge throughout England were only just being constructed and not opened in York until the 1840s. The first line from London only reached York in 1840 via Normanton, (with a connection to Leeds via Milford) but the direct line to Leeds was not opened until 1869. Prior to the railway, travel anywhere was slow and expensive. John Phillips clearly had remarkable stamina to give courses of lectures throughout cities of the North, sometimes travelling across the Pennines two or three times a week, to fulfil his lecturing engagements.

Charles Babbage

Another major challenge and demand on his time was to emerge. It began when the mathematician Charles Babbage, (1791–1871), Lucasian Professor of Mathematics at Cambridge, the designer of the world's first pre-electronic computer, published in 1830 **Reflections on the Decline of Science in England**:

> *It cannot have escaped the attention of those, whose acquirements enable them to judge, and who have had opportunities of examining the state of science in other countries, that in England, with respect to the more difficult and abstract sciences, we are much below other nations, not merely of equal rank, but below several even of inferior power*[7]

As its title suggests, this was a polemic against the failure of the learned societies – including the Royal Society – to promote the advance of scientific ideas. His complaints were strongly supported by Sir David Brewster (1781–1868) of Edinburgh, the distinguished scientist, author and enthusiastic promoter of early techniques of photography. In reviewing **Reflections**, Brewster tore into the Government and the universities for their complacent neglect of science and indeed of scientists themselves who lacked recognition and often (like William Smith) basic financial support:

> *"there is not a single philosopher who enjoys a pension or allowance, or a sinecure, capable of supporting him and his family in the humblest circumstances"*.[8]

Sir David Brewster

Babbage had attended a meeting of the Deutscher Naturforscher Versammlung – an association of leading German men of science who were doing much to encourage national awareness of scientific ideas in Germany with annual meetings in different cities in pre-unified Germany. Following a suggestion from another energetic Scotsman J.F.W. Johnson, who had attended the Hamburg DNV meeting in 1830, the three scientists took a decision to seek support from the Yorkshire Philosophical Society. Brewster had recently collaborated with YPS on a research project in astronomy, and in February 1831 he wrote to their Secretary John Phillips asking the Yorkshire Philosophical Society if they would be willing to promote such a gathering of *"Men of Science"*.[9]

The Council of the Yorkshire Philosophical Society, encouraged by Harcourt and Phillips, responded to the idea enthusiastically, and offered the facilities of their impressive new Museum with its suite of spacious room and gas-lit lecture theatre as an excellent location.[10] Support came from other leading figures such as the astronomer William Herschel, William Whewell, Professor of Mathematics at Cambridge, Adam Sedgwick, and Roderick Murchison, by then President of the Geological Society, as well as from the Mayor of York itself.

Brewster and Babbage soon felt what was being proposed by Harcourt and the YPS was somewhat less radical than the organisation they had in mind. But Harcourt, ever the pragmatist, was concerned that they needed to be more moderate in their approach to succeed if they were to attract the support of the leading politicians and opinion formers at this critical initial stage.

The decision was taken to agree to host the first meeting in York and invitations were issued to academic institutes, learned bodies and individual scientists from all over Britain to come to the city for a Foundation Meeting.

This first formal Meeting, after registration of attendees the day before, took place in the Museum on Tuesday 27th September 1831. Events relating to the Meeting were to continue over the rest of that week.

Despite continued scepticism from some quarters, most especially in London, the Foundation Meeting in York was a considerable success. Even though several of the giants of the scientific establishment such as Herschel, Faraday, Buckland, Whewell, Babbage and Sedgwick (who was actually in Snowdonia giving what would be crucial tuition to a young Charles Darwin on the core principles of geology) either absented themselves or were not able to attend through prior commitments, many other key people did attend. These included Murchison, and the great John Dalton, from Manchester, the father of atomic theory, Charles Daubeny the chemist and botanist from Oxford, and David Brewster. What really mattered was the presence of over 200 individual "philosophers" mainly from the north of England, from the Societies in Leeds, Sheffield, Hull, Liverpool and Manchester as well as York itself. YPS President Lord Milton took the chair. As well as lectures on a wide range of scientific topics, including papers from John Dalton and Roderick Murchison and specialists on a wide range of other topics, there were animated discussions, readings of memoirs and scientific papers, and conversations. In addition was the kind of networking which forms a prime function of all modern academic and scientific conferences and seminars, an opportunity for experts in various fields to meet their peers and share the latest ideas and information in convivial surroundings.

This was also a unique opportunity for the Yorkshire Philosophical Society to show off its fine new Museum which was admired by the guests. It was also a chance for the city of York to show of its rich architectural and cultural heritage.

The hospitality, which was spread around York to the Assembly Rooms, to local clubs, hotels and taverns was lavish. Many guests were put up by individual YPS members in their homes. Lord Milton and David Brewster were fortunate enough to enjoy the grand surrounding of the Bishop's Palace at Bishopthorpe staying with the Harcourts. There were extravagant dinners and concerts to entertain the scientists and their ladies, and discussion and conviviality went on into the late hours.

York's elegant eighteenth-century Assembly Rooms designed by Lord Burlington

One of the stars of the whole event was John Phillips who gave an eloquent, learned and impromptu lecture to the gathering which as reported in the York Gazette was:

> "on the Geology of Yorkshire – got up on the spur of the moment, without any premeditation, and which showed the complete mastery he has of the science".[11]

As Sir Roderick Murchison was later to recall:

> I may say that it was the cheerful and engaging manners of young Phillips that went far in cementing us, and even then he gave signs of the eminence to which he afterwards arose in the numerous years in which he was the most efficient assistant general secretary.[12]

The other star of the whole meeting was its deviser and master of ceremonies Vernon Harcourt who, in a brilliant speech, laid out an impressive ground plan for the new Association which he presented to all attendees.[13]

In his proposal to establish the Association Harcourt suggested the new body should:

> *have for its objects, to give a stronger impulse and more systematic direction to scientific inquiry, to obtain more national attention to the objects of science, and a removal of those disadvantages which impede its progress, and to promote the intercourse of the cultivation of science with one another, and with foreign philosophers.*[14]

It is worth noting how from such an early date the founders of the Association fully understood the international nature of science and scientific research. True science, like nature itself, crosses all national boundaries.

With such fine words and sentiment, the British Association for the Advancement of Science (BAAS) was created, as a force for enlightened scientific thinking and progressive ideas throughout the British Isles and beyond. Very much based on the German model, it was built around the concept of its meetings being hosted in provincial capitals and centres throughout the country, hereby acting as a major stimulus to local activity and collaborative research in many different scientific disciplines. These were to be the responsibility of separate Sections each with their own officers.

Not entirely surprisingly, Harcourt and Phillips were duly elected as Vice President and Assistant Secretary respectively, a post Phillips retained until 1859. They had the immediate challenge of turning their words into hard reality. A report of the Foundation Meeting was duly prepared, published and circulated in February 1833, and was well received. As well as setting out the Constitution of the new body, the document contained learned reports on the progress of various sciences by leading experts in their respective fields – a practice which continues to this day. Harcourt and Phillips, responding on the initial stimulus of Babbage and Brewster, had established a body which, through its annual meetings and communications, including its important Annual Reports, was to become one of the leading and most influential scientific organisations in Britain and Europe.

The Observatory in the Yorkshire Museum Gardens

It was also very much a development, on a national level, of the ideas of the Yorkshire philosophers, and of Harcourt and Phillips in particular. A congratulatory message from the British Association for the Advancement of Science sent to the Yorkshire Philosophical Society at its centenary in 1922 commented *"the Society ... is justly regarded by the Association as its mother society".*[15]

It is difficult to overstress the importance of the BAAS in establishing, in a pre-internet age, a vital communication network between specialists in all the sciences encouraged by their annual gatherings, Annual Reports, and personal contact. In addition the Association's gatherings facilitated and encouraged Government lobbying of scientific interests.

Such Annual Conferences, as we would term them today, have become a template for many other scholarly and professional bodies and associations, part of a necessary structure to enable the emergence of a new professional class, now so familiar in the twentieth and twenty-first centuries, of academics able to live by their intellectual efforts.

The British Association for the Advancement of Science also enabled John Phillips to move from a regional to a national stage. His outstanding work in geology and other disciplines, through the BAAS and other networks, became widely known to the scientific establishment. Recognition and honours were soon to follow. In 1834 he was elected – with Buckland, Murchison and Sedgwick among his sponsors – as a Fellow of the Royal Society, to allow him to use the letters FRS after his name, and in 1834 to the Chair of Geology at Kings College London. His meteoric rise from humble Assistant Mineral Surveyor to a Professorship at a leading university in a mere 10 years, and to do so without any formal qualification, must be almost unprecedented in academic history. He accepted the job in part to have the by-now prestigious title of "Professor" on his many publications, but also to have a secure form of income, as the lectures in London paid well. The memory of his teenage years and the precarious hand-to mouth finances of his uncle played a major part in Phillips' almost fanatical work ethic.

He could still combine his teaching role in London for a few weeks in the year with his work for the YPS and the Yorkshire Museum. He supervised the erection of the Observatory in the Museum Gardens in 1833. Sadly the atmospheric pollution of York made this observatory less successful than had been hoped, but Phillips soon had the loan of a fine 6¼ inch refractory telescope especially made for him by his friend the York instrument maker Thomas Cooke, which he used in his own garden. On 18th July in 1853 he took only the second-ever detailed published photograph of the surface of the Moon, using a recently invented wet collodion process. The image was exhibited at the 23rd BAAS meeting in Hull in September that year.

Roger Hutchins[16] has suggested that both through his moon photographs and in his work using his own photos and drawings of the surface of Mars (Phillips produced the first British accurate map of Mars), Phillips made a major contribution to nineteenth century astronomy and comparative planetology, the forerunner of modern space science. This was in addition to his outstanding work to support the science through the BAAS. Few other British geologists have a ring of mountains on the moon and two features on Mars named after them.[17]

Above: The Phillips Crater on the surface of the moon named after John Phillips (James Stuby, based on a NASA image)
Right: John Phillips' pioneering photograph of the moon taken from his garden in York in 1853 (©The Royal Society/BAAS)

On more earthly matters, Phillips was soon making York a centre of meteorological study, designing and making improved types of rain gauges to reduce water loss through evaporation. These were located at key points in the Museum Gardens and at various locations in and around York, including the top of the Minster tower. This initiative allowed him to correlate rainfall levels with the seasons and with air temperatures recorded at the same time, but also with height above sea level. He recruited members of YPS and other local Societies to become weather recorders in the York area. Dating from the 1830s these are among the earliest reliable British weather records and are of continuing scientific interest as climate change is monitored. He regularly presented results from his own weather research and recording at the Annual Meetings of the BAAS, for example reporting on the results of an experiment situating rain gauges in York at different heights away from buildings in order to prove there was heavier precipitation at lower levels closer to the ground.[18]

Increasingly Phillips was forced to hand over Museum responsibilities to his Sub Curator Henry Baines. Arduous administrative work and correspondence for the BAAS which included planning for the Annual Meetings and editing and publishing the often voluminous Annual Reports (he edited no less than 27 of the Association's Annual reports in total) were an increasing drain on his scarce time and energy.

In 1840 he was appointed to the recently established Geological Survey. He finally resigned from his post with the YPS in 1842 but remained as an Honorary Keeper for the Museum until 1844 and kept his close links with the Society for the rest of his life.

On the recommendation of Henry de la Beche, Director of the Geological Survey, Phillips was invited to examine the organic remains of the older strata of western England. Phillips, passionate field geologist, clearly relished the idea of working outdoors exploring what would for him be a relatively unknown part of England. In 1841 he published what seemed like an obscure publication **Figures and Description of Palaeozoic Fossils of Cornwall, Devon and West Somerset.**

Yet this was a piece of work of world importance. As well as giving detailed descriptions of all the various fossils in their relevant locations and strata, and using the kind of statistical palaeontology of which he was a master, Phillips teased out what was to become the worldwide classification of the first great periods of life on earth:

> That one great system of organic life belongs to the older, that is, in general terms, to the "Primary" and "transition" strata, has long been known. Mr Murchison, after adding immensely to the previous catalogue of these fossils, calls part of the series to which his attention was most directed "protozoic" for which Professor Sedgwick proposed to substitute "Palaeozoic". I have suggested the propriety of extending the application of this term to make it include not only the "Silurian" group, but all the newer types of organism to the magnesian limestone; and following out this plan of nomenclature I have presented an outline of a general classification of the evidence of the organic remains which fortunately clashes very little with the ordinary scheme founded on structural, mineral and chemical analogies of the rocks. As this classification will be employed in some of the following pages, it is here offered in the original form – proposed titles depending on the series of organic affinities:

> **Upper Plieocene Tertiaries**

> **Cainozoic Strata** – Middle Meiocene Tertiaires, lower Eocene Tertiaries, Upper Cretaceous system

> **Mesozoic Strata** – Middle Oolitic system, lower new Red formation, Upper Magnesian Limestone formation, Carboniferous systems

> **Palaeozoic Strata**; Middle (Eifel and South Devon), Lower Transition Strata, Primary Strata[19]

These terms describing the origins of life on our planet have endured, and are now the standard worldwide nomenclature for the early periods of recorded life on earth – being in descending order – Cainozoic or the period of newer life to include mammals, Mesozoic – a term that Phillips invented – the middle period that brought reptiles including the great dinosaurs, and the Palaeozoic being the era of early life forms including plants, sea creatures and primitive fish.

Geological Scale of Time.

Periods.	Systems.	Life.
Cænozoic.	Pleistocene.	Man.
	Pleiocene.	Placental Mammals.
	Meiocene.	
	Eocene.	
Mesozoic.	Cretaceous.	
	Oolitic.	Marsupial Mammals.
	Triassic.	
Palæozoic.	Permian.	
	Carboniferous.	Reptiles.
	Devonian.	Land Plants. Fishes.
	Siluro-Cambrian.	Monomy. Echinod. Pterop. Heterop. Dimy. Gasterop. Annel. Polyzoa. Zooph. Brach. Crust.

List of early epochs of life

But Phillips' work goes further. Hull University geologist and science journalist Dr. Liam Herringshaw has used the term "York's Time Lord" to describe John Phillips' exploration of the concept of geological or "deep time" through careful statistical analysis of the palaeontological and stratigraphical evidence.[20]

In his book **Life on Earth: Its Origin and Succession** published in 1860, and stimulated by the Rede Lecture he had given at Cambridge in that same year, Phillips calculated the possible date of the earth, based on calculations of the rate of erosion of rocks over many aeons, to be between 60 and 96 million years.[21] [22] Charles Darwin had already suggested however that the age of the earth was even older. His calculation in **The Origin of Species** that the rate of erosion in the Kentish Weald was at least 300 million years but *"in all probability a far longer period than 300 million years has elapsed since the latter part of the Secondary period.*[23]*"* Darwin was closer to what we now know to be the truth.

But in common with most other progressive Christian-humanist thinkers of his time, Phillips' writings supported the view that life on earth as we know it has occupied a very small portion of our planet's immense lifespan. As the science writer Michael Roberts has argued:[24]

Most educated Christians, whether Anglican or not, accepted modern science, especially geology, although a few opposed "old-Earth" geology on theological grounds.

For John Phillips saw no conflict between his Christian beliefs and his geological research. It was the role of scientific enquiry to reveal God's purposes and for him there were no contradictions with his beliefs wherever the quest for knowledge might lead. Progressive Christian thinkers believed the Old Testament to be a powerful mixture of Hebrew legend and history, full of moral truth, but not to be understood literally. Genesis was a metaphor, not scientific fact, though God was still very much involved in the process of Creation and was keeping a watchful eye on the world.

But there were fundamentalists (as there still are in many parts of the world) who passionately believed the world was created, according to the calculation of the seventeenth century theologian Bishop James Ussher, only 6,000 years ago, or to be astonishingly precise at 0900 on Monday October 4th 4004 BC.[25]

This clash of beliefs between fundamentalists and liberals came to a head at the second meeting of the British Association in York in 1844. The Dean of York, William Cockburn, was incensed by the 1836 Bridgewater Treatise **Geology and Mineralogy considered with reference to Natural Theology** by William Buckland which sought to explain the development of species as successive divine interventions. Cockburn regarded Buckland's essay as blasphemy.[26] An exchange of opinions took place in the BA Geology Section in the third day of the meeting in the recently renovated Hospitium, when the Dean gave an address which in its wild excesses quoted Moses and *"could not be listened to with gravity from anyone acquainted with the science"* and was greeted with laughter from the learned scientists present.

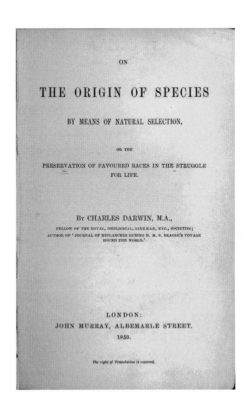

Professor Adam Sedgwick, himself an ordained clergyman and a Dean of Norwich Cathedral, gave the devastating response on behalf of the Association, shredding the hapless Cockburn in an address which was scholarly, witty and not without ridicule. Undeterred Cockburn published his essay in a notorious pamphlet **The Bible versus the British Association** which was widely distributed and avidly read. As Sedgwick's Victorian biographers, Thomas Willis Clark & Professor Thomas McKenny Hughes, were later to comment:

> *Ignorant and foolish as Dean Cockburn was, it is easy to see from the number of editions of his pamphlet published in the course of a few weeks, that he represented the feelings of a large majority of his countrymen.*[27]

Wisely perhaps, John Phillips, as the diplomatic servant of an Association which had many clergymen among its members, avoided the divisive arguments and there is no reference to the debate in the 1844 BAAS Annual Report, though there is little doubt that most scientists present would have sided with Sedgwick and Buckland.

But it was an argument that was not to go away. When in 1859 Charles Darwin published **On the Origin of Species,** the Christian humanists were on the other side, being far from convinced that Darwin's great theory of Evolution was much more than a new version of the popular but largely discredited theory of the transmutation of species of Robert Chambers in his **Vestiges of the Natural History of Creation** of 1844.[28] It led to perhaps the most famous British Association meeting in its history when in 1861 at the Oxford meeting, Thomas Huxley took on Bishop Wilberforce over the contentious issue of man's descent from the apes.

Though Phillips admired Darwin as a natural scientist and could accept and support much of what Darwin wrote, (they had frequent correspondence), ultimately he could not accept that a world and universe that sustained such immense natural beauty and which had produced humanity and so many great achievements in science and the arts was the result of random accidents of electricity and chemistry without a "directing mind".[29] He believed fundamentally that the purpose of science was to both observe and understand the two great phenomena that for him determined life on earth – the Force of Nature and the Laws of Nature – that logically to him suggested a primaeval act of Creation by a single Mind or Almighty Being.

His criticism of Darwin – who claimed major gaps in the paleontological evidence base that Phillips disputed (though Darwin was later proved to be correct) – was part of a wide ranging review in **Life on Earth** published in 1860 only a year after the publication of **Origin of Species**. This included his thoughts at that time of the published views of all the major thinkers on the origins of life, including Lyell, Lamarck, Cuvier, Sedgwick, Agassiz and others. He makes a cogent argument against what he saw as the naïve application of the pure theory of Natural Selection:

> *if Natural Selection be thus gifted with the power of continually acting for the good of its subject – encouraging it or rather compelling it to continual advancement … How is this beneficial personification to be separated from an ever watchful Providence…?*

He therefore suggests if the word "creation" has to used, it should stand for:

> *a confession of our own ignorance of the way in which the governing mind has in this case acted on matter.*[30]

But as James Davies argued,[31] by the 1870s the basic arguments contained within **On The Origin of the Species**, had become far more widely accepted among the scientific community, and was being increasingly supported by evidence gathered by leading naturalists from throughout the world. Even Phillips had endorsed Thomas Huxley's view of bird-like features of a saurian reptile which Huxley – a leading proponent of Darwin's theories – construed being as a vital missing link in the evolution of birds.[32]

In 1873 in Bradford, in his capacity as President of the Geology Section, at what was to be his final address to the British Association, Phillips could write:

> *Similitude, not identity, is the effect of natural agencies in the continuation of life forms, the small difference from identity*

Charles Darwin

being due to limited physical conditions, in harmony with the general law that organic structures are adapted to the exigencies of being. Moreover the structures are adaptable to new conditions; if the conditions change, the structures may change also, but not suddenly; the plant or animal may survive in presence of slowly altered circumstances, but must perish under critical inversions. These adaptations, so necessary for the preservation of a race, are they restricted within narrow limits? Or is it possible that in the course of long enduring time, step by step and grain by grain, one form of life can be changed and has been changed, and has been changed to another and adapted to fulfil quite different function?[33]

He goes on to suggest the critical role of geology in determining the truth or otherwise of Darwinism:

> *and in particular exposition of it by the great naturalist whose name it bears, because it alone possesses the history of the development in time, and to the accumulated effect of small but almost infinitely numerous changes in certain directions, that the full effect of the transformation is attributed.*

It was the task of the geologist to collect *"with fidelity"* the evidence needed to prove the theory of Natural Selection. If not a ringing endorsement, it was close to a cautious acceptance. Darwin, Phillips had now conceded, was indeed *"the great naturalist"*.

As the American science historian Michon Scott suggests:

> *Scientists continue to debate how accurately fossils record life's diversity, but so far the conclusions Phillips reached appear to have largely withstood the test of time.*[34]

Over a century and a half later our perspectives have changed. Enriched by concepts of ecology, natural biodiversity, symbiosis between species, and even James Lovelock' Gaia theory,[35] Darwinism is no longer seen to be purely about survival of the fittest, however so defined. Many contemporary scientists of many different religious backgrounds can now also accept Darwin's great theory without losing their faith and belief in a personal God. Current genetic research may give them some support. Phillips would recognise Genetic Drift theory, with its underlying complex mathematical patterns, as indeed reflecting his Laws of Nature. And with the age of the earth now calculated to be around 4.5 billion years, and the Universe believed to have been created by what is known as the "Big Bang" or sudden cataclysmic event, that many astro-physicists suggest happened some 13.8 billion years ago, theories of Creation and therefore even a Creative Force, however so defined, no longer seem quite as outlandish or absurd as they did a generation ago.

As nature writer Robert Macfarlane describes in his book **Underland**, in the pristine silence of a salt chamber deep in Boulby Potash Mile, less than a mile from where John Phillips examined the rock structure and fossils of the Yorkshire coast at Staithes and Boulby cliffs, astro-physicists are currently exploring the nature of so-called Dark Matter, lost in deep time, in order to attempt to reveal the mysterious origins of the Universe.[36]

Phillips had argued that it was the continuing role of science to constantly ask questions about the earth and the universe within which it is contained, and to use whatever new technological innovations that are available to the scientist to seek new evidence and to re-examine old. This would ultimately reveal greater

John Phillips when President of the Geological Society in 1859–60 (British Geological Survey collection)

understanding of what he believed to be an ordered Universe controlled by the rational hand of Divine Wisdom.

Even if we no longer share Phillips' confident Christian-humanist beliefs, the principles behind empirical, evidence-based scientific research remain as profoundly true for the twenty-first century as they did for the nineteenth. The role of the British Association for the Advancement of Science to enable fellow scientists to continue their work in safety, economic security and freedom, with the support and co-operation of their peers, continues as a guiding principle long after the death of its most influential founding figures.

In 2009 the BAAS became the British Science Association. Its annual gathering of scientists from countries throughout the world is now known as the British Science Festival, one of the biggest of its kind in Europe. The event continues to be hosted in different towns and cities throughout the UK, giving an invigorating boost to scientific activity and research in every city or major town that hosts the event. In addition, there is a special British Science Week that takes place to promote an awareness and interest in science among the public and especially among young people. It also works regionally through local and regional partners and associates such as the Yorkshire Philosophical Society, as well as nationally through Government agencies to influence policies and to further the cause of scientific thinking and education throughout the British Isles.

William Vernon Harcourt and John Phillips had lit a beacon in 1831 in York which continues to blaze in Britain through the twenty-first century, as brightly as it did nearly two centuries ago.

Notes

1   Yorkshire Gazette 6th February 1830

2   Morrell Jack 2005 *John Phillips and the business of Victorian Science* Aldershot: Ashgate p96

3   *Ibid.* p119

4   Allen David Elliston 1976 *The Naturalist in Britain* pp73–93

5   Morrell Jack 2005 *op. cit.* p128

6   Scott Machin 2019 *Rocky Road: John Phillips* in www.strangescience.net/phillips.htm

7   Babbage Charles 1830 *Reflections on the Decline of Science in England and some of its causes*: Introductory remarks. London: Fellowes p1

8   Brewster D in Edinburgh Review Vol Xiii p305 quoted in Howarth O.J. R 1931

9   Orange A.D. *1973 Philosophers and Provincials The Yorkshire Philosophical Society from 1822–1844* York: YPS pp32–39

10 Rubinstein David 2009 *The Nature of the World – the Yorkshire Philosophical Society 1822–2000* York:YPS p13

11 Orange A.D.Op. cit p37

12 Geike Archibald quoted by Davis 1889 in *History of the Yorkshire Geological and Polytechnic Society 1837–88* p127

13 Quoted in Howarth O.J.R 1931 The British Association for the Advancement of Science: A Retrospect 1831–1931. London: British Association p16–25p

14 Howarth O.J.R 1931 *ibid.* p16–17

15 Orange Op. Cit p32

16 Hutchins Roger 2012 *John Phillips's astronomy 1852–67, a pioneering contribution to comparative planetology* in The Antiquarian Astronomer (Science History Publications) Issue 8 January 2012 p44–57.

17 Morrell Jack 2005 *op. cit.* p378

18 BAAS 1834 *Fourth Annual Report Transaction of the Sections* pp560–61; BAAS 1845 Fifteenth Annual report Transactions of the Sections p21

19 Phillips J. 1841 *Figures and Description of Palaeozoic Fossils of Cornwall, Devon and West Somerset* London: Longman, Brown, Green & Longman pp160–161

20 Herringshaw Liam 2013: www.yorkmix.com/uncategorized/saluting-pioneer-john-phillips-the-time-lord-of-york

21 Phillips John 1860 *Life on Earth: Its origin and succession.* Cambridge & London: Macmillan p126

22 Rudwick Martin 2014 *Earth's Deep History – How it was discovered and why it matters.* Chicago& London: Chicago University Press p230–231

23 Darwin Charles 1959 *On the Origin of Species* London: Macmillan p297

24 Roberts M.B 2009 *Adam Sedgwick (1785–1873) Geologist and Evangelist –* Geological Society of London Special Publications Vol 310 p156

25 Ussher James 1658 *The Annals of the Old Testament from the Beginning of the World* (in https://ia800708.us.archive.org/12/items/AnnalsOfTheWorld/Annals.pdf)

26 Manning Phillip Lars 2001: *John Phillips (1800–1874) in Yorkshire People and Places* YPS p123

27 Clark John Willis and Hughes Thomas McKenny 1890: *The Life and Letters of Adam Sedgwick* Vol 2 p78

28 Chambers Robert 1844 *Vestiges of the Natural History of Creation*

29 Phillips John 1860 Op.Cit. p208

30 *Ibid.* p216

31 Davis James W. 1882 *Proceedings of the Yorkshire Geological and Polytechnic Society* Vol 8 part 1 p18

32 Morrell Jack 2005 Op.cit p498

33 British Association 1874 *Annual Report 1873 Transcriptions of the Sections* pp73–4

34 Scott Mahon 2019 Op. Cit.

35 Lovelock James 1979 Gaia: *A New Look at Life on Earth*: Oxford: OUP 197)

36 Macfarlane Robert (t2019) Underland London@ Hamish Hamilton pp55–78

Mountain (Great Scar) Limestone strata exposed at
Twistleton Scars, near Ingleton (Dorian Speakman)

5

The Yorkshire Dales

Illustrations of the Geology of Yorkshire Part II the Mountain
Limestone District was published in 1836, by London publishers
John Murray, seven years after the first volume of **Illustrations of the
Geology of Yorkshire – The Yorkshire Coast.**

If Phillips had planned to produce this second volume when he published
the first, there was no indication of this in the first volume. But the idea
had preoccupied him for some time. As early as 1832 he had already
issued a Prospectus to attract subscriptions for this second volume, which
was to focus on North West Yorkshire, with a plan to have the book in
print by 1833. But it took another three years before the book was finally
published.

What is remarkable is not that the book was delayed for three years
but that it appeared at all. Phillips was a workaholic, and his energy
and activities were prodigious. In addition to his job as Keeper of the
Museum, with all that this role entailed in terms of supervising the
collections and the activities of the honorary curators, as well as many
administrative tasks, including routine maintenance of the buildings
and grounds, by now he was also the paid Assistant Secretary of the
British Association for the Advancement of Science. He had to deal
with various committees, liaise with fellow officers, deal with research
grants and each summer take on the huge amount of work relating to
the Annual Meetings. He also had to produce and edit the Association's
Annual Report which was far more than a report of meetings but, in its

A

GUIDE TO GEOLOGY.

BY

JOHN PHILLIPS, F.R.S. G.S.,

PROFESSOR OF GEOLOGY IN KING'S COLLEGE, LONDON ;

SECRETARY TO THE YORKSHIRE PHILOSOPHICAL SOCIETY ;

ASSISTANT SECRETARY TO THE BRITISH ASSOCIATION FOR THE ADVANCEMENT
OF SCIENCE.

" Et mare contrahitur, siccæque est campus arenæ
Quod modo pontus erat, quosque altum texerat æquor
Existunt montes."—Ov. *Metam.*

LONDON:

PRINTED FOR

LONGMAN, REES, ORME, BROWN, GREEN, AND LONGMAN.

---

detailed Proceedings, a research publication in its own right. He also played a leading role in the Geology and Physical Science Sections, encouraging the sharing of idea and research in these areas, which included topics such as Magnetism and Astronomy. In between all this activity he had to squeeze his own research, endless programmes of public lectures, and the writing of articles, including contributions on geology to various popular encyclopaedias, into whatever few hours of day or night were available.

Yet he prioritised in what scarce spare time he had the writing and publishing of a popular and still highly readable short textbook on the new science of geology, aimed at both the general reader and also the more informed student. Published by Longman in 1834, the **Guide to Geology**, dedicated "*to the members of the Yorkshire Philosophical Society – by one who has long laboured for them and with them in advancing the love and knowledge of Nature*", sets out to define and introduce geology to a wider audience in clear, straightforward prose. This was to define and outline the nature of the science, illustrated with examples not just from Britain but from throughout the world. As he states in the Preface:

> *I wish to exclude from this little volume, all discussions of theory, and yet to embody in it those important references, once debated, but now established, which give Geology consistence of reason, clearness of description and an acknowledged place in the circle of inductive science.*[1]

The book achieves exactly this intention and is still a highly readable text and summary for layperson and expert alike. In its chapters on the main types of rock sections and their characteristic palaeontology, it also points the reader towards the work of other contemporary writers and researchers in the field, and locations such as museums where key collections of fossil plants and fauna could be seen. The Yorkshire Museum, rightly, features significantly. Not surprisingly, **The Guide to Geology** proved extremely popular and ran to three editions, being republished in 1836 and 1837.

His Professorship at King's College London only required him to spend a few weeks in London which could, in theory, be fitted in with his Yorkshire activities. In fact, it put a huge strain on him in terms of time, and by 1835 he was struggling to cope with lecturing demands, only reluctantly agreeing to give a course of eight lectures in London at a time when he was desperate to finish the next volume of his **Illustrations**.

Attermire Scar, Settle, along mid Craven Fault (Dorian Speakman)

The other reason the Mountain Limestone book took so long to appear is that it was, and remains, a huge intellectual achievement, a milestone in the history of British geology in terms of its understanding and unravelling of the great karst limestone scenery of northwest Yorkshire. This required extensive field research and meticulous observation of the complex patterns of strata, including the impact of the great faulting system through Craven; Phillips was among the first to accurately describe the Craven Fault. These were some of the oldest rock systems to be described at that period, lying above the more ancient Silurian and Cambrian systems being unravelled by Murchison and Sedgwick at much the same time.

This was a landscape which Phillips had fallen in love with in 1819 when he first came with his uncle to what are now known as the Yorkshire Dales on a visit to the Auld Gang lead mine in Swaledale, where he was able to compare Yorkshire limestones with those he had seen in Gloucestershire and South Wales. Two years later, in 1821, he walked with his uncle from Derbyshire to the Lake District through some of the karst limestone landscapes of Craven which left a deep impression on him. He got to know the area in far greater detail when they were based in Kirkby Lonsdale, the starting point for so many of their geological excursions into the Craven highlands.

In the introduction to **Mountain Limestone**, Phillips lists no less than seventeen separate and subsequent geological surveys he had made in researching the book, many lasting several days and even weeks. All this time he was making detailed notes, measuring the heights of fells and crags, identifying strata and unravelling faults, collecting and identifying fossils. These surveys were initially made with his uncle, but increasingly on his own or with friends such as Edward George or M.de Billy from Strasbourg. There were also trips to Ireland, Belgium, Luxembourg and Strasbourg, Geneva and Lyon to both make comparisons with British limestones and types and locations of fossils.

At the end of this impressive record of his extensive wanderings he notes:

> *In the course of so many pedestrian journeys most of the*
> *high mountains have been ascended, and nearly every valley*

explored; the thickness of the strata having been ascertained by
above one thousand barometrical observations.

In the hope the proceeding sketch of my proceedings will be
thought to justify my publications; the nature of the subjects
investigated of so many hills and dales, combined with that
want of leisure, which so fatally retards the progress of men
devoted to science, must be my apology for the long delay of its
appearance.[2]

The distances covered by Phillips in his extended researches on foot
must make him, in terms of the central and northern Pennines, supreme
among hill and fell walkers of all time – someone whose detailed
knowledge and understanding of the varied landscapes of the Yorkshire
Dales has probably rarely, if ever, been surpassed.

He even quotes, to justify his work, that other great wanderer of our
Northern fells, poet if not quite geologist, William Wordsworth:

Enough if something from our hands have power
To live, and act, and serve the future hour."[3]

a sentiment that Phillips suggests is *"peculiarly applicable to the labours of*
all men of science".

Inevitably later generations of geologists, including of course the
Geological Survey for whom Phillips was later to work in south west
England, with far more human resources and equipment, would
constantly improve, refine and revise Phillips' pioneering work.
But he had laid the foundations of so much of our knowledge of the
understanding of the Yorkshire Dales landscape, insights too easily taken
for granted by later generations.

In his wanderings and research, Phillips was always ready to meet
his fellow geologists and palaeontologists, amateur and professional.
He would quote and make full use of their knowledge and expertise,
especially local fossil collections which would provide a valuable cross-
reference with his own work. However, such help was always fully
acknowledged, his sources named and thanked. He was even able to
have the book's content discussed at the 1835 Dublin Meeting of the

Malham Tarn on the mid Craven Fault. It was created by glacial meltwaters forming a mighty cataract, 80 metres high and 300 metres long (author)

British Association with a peer group that included Adam Sedgwick (to whom the book was dedicated, jointly with William Vernon Harcourt), Roderick Murchison, Charles Daubeney and Jean Louis Agassiz.

Unlike the first **Illustrations – The Yorkshire Coast**, Phillips dispenses with a long introductory chapter on the nature of geological science, as this was already fully covered in the earlier volume, and but also by his own 1834 **Guide to Geology.**

The wealth of detail in the book still impresses. The first chapter, **Description of the Rocks Deposited in Water** lists all the characteristic sedimentary rocks of the region, in their ascending stratigraphically order, together with exact measurements, in tabular form of the thickness of individual strata at particular sites.

He begins from the earliest rocks, ancient slates – by this stage given their recognised, newly established names Cambrian and Silurian following the recent papers by Sedgwick and Murchison, noting how these were generally to be found in the western fringes of the Dales, from west of Kirkby Lonsdale and into the Howgills. He also describes the narrow band of slates which runs due eastwards from Kirkby Lonsdale across to Ribblesdale, lying underneath the gigantic limestone plateau that supports Whernside, Ingleborough and Pen-y-Ghent. Using evidence from quarry faces as well as exposed scars, he offers detailed technical explanation of the fault lines and fractures that have produced so many distinctive karst landforms of crag and scar, such as along the Ribblesdale edges and around Malham.

Then follows a detailed description of the Carboniferous System of the Dales, which as he explains derives its name from the most characteristic of its products, coal, *"not that every part of this is series is productive of this valuable substance"*.

He starts from the Old Red Sandstones and conglomerates exposed along the borders with Cumberland and Westmorland, ascending to both the Mountain Limestone – now generally known as Great Scar Limestone – to the Yoredale Series and finally the Millstone Grits that cap the high fells.

Mountain Limestone was part of the title of his book and it was as an authority on Yorkshire limestone that Phillips' reputation as one of Britain's greatest geologists was to be made. As he says:

> *The mountain limestone may be considered as peculiarly a British rock; for its extent in our island is far greater than in all the rest of Europe. The study of it is full of curious interest, and the variations which it presents appear well calculated to suggest correct views as to the changing condition of ocean and land during one geological period[4]*

Gordale Scar – sketch by Phillips

He divides the limestones of the Dales as perhaps the best examples of Carboniferous Limestone in England into two distinct groups. The northern series has an Upper Limestone group over 1,000 feet thick and is "complicated". In the south things are a little simpler. The southern group is divided from the north by an approximate line from Jervaulx Abbey in Wensleydale, across Coverdale to Kettlewell, Littondale and Ryleloaf Hill near Malham, then westwards towards Lancaster. It is the great geological fault lines between the two which produce so much of the most spectacular landscape of the Yorkshire Dales, the crags and escarpments of Malhamdale, Ribblesdale, Crummackdale and above Ingleton, as well as exposing the extensive limestone pavements of Ingleborough and Whernside.

North and west of the Jervaulx-Malham line lies the more complex northern group or upper series. Here the limestones were given a different name by Phillips:

> We shall choose, as a general standard of reference for this complex series of rocks, that district where this character of complexity is the greatest. The upper end of Wensleydale is therefore adopted. The total thickness of the limestone series in this situation is about one thousand feet and it consists of the following groups (a table follows) constituting what I term THE YOREDALE SERIES.[5]

Then follows the tables of strata and where these are to be seen in Wensleydale, Swaledale and Teesdale.

The next section is devoted to the gritstone landscapes, created by newer sandstone rocks which rest above the Yoredale series and which dominate the eastern dales – the moorland ridges of Swaledale, Wensleydale, Wharfedale, Barden, Nidderdale, Brimham Rocks, the summits of Pen Hill, Flasby Fell, Great Whernside, Fountains Fell, Pendle Hill to the south, and to the south west the Forest of Bowland.

Oxclose Scar, Wensleydale, demonstrating the classic step erosion of the Yoredale Limestones. See page 112 also (author)

Upper Wharfedale – looking across to the gritstone summit of Old Cote Moor (author)

Chapter II, titled **Basaltic Rocks, Dykes and Mineral Veins** is still focused on rock types and devoted to the characteristic igneous rocks mainly to the north of the Dales that include the Whin Sill intrusions in Tynedale and Teesdale. Parts of Teesdale were within the boundaries of Yorkshire until 1974 and he gives a fine description of High Force waterfall. There is also a section on mineralisation and the many productive veins of minerals such as galena (lead ore) and calamine (zinc ore) which were so important in the industries of Upper Wharfedale, Malham, Nidderdale and Swaledale.

Chapter III **Symmetrical Structure of Rocks** looks in detail at the jointing and structure of the rocks of the Pennines, whilst Chapter IV **Effects of Subterranean Movement** examines the impacts, on the surface, of subterranean earth movements and faults so characteristic of the Dales, as illustrated by the Pennine and Craven Faults.

This chapter includes a fine early description of the Craven Fault which he noted, *"arising from two slips and one very deep dip"* under Ingleborough being:

*not less than three thousand feet, above Settle one thousand,
and it diminishes towards Grassington, where numerous other
dislocations confuse but do not destroy its effects.*[6]

This was clear evidence to Phillips that in remote times past there had been a series of profound and relatively sudden events, such as fault movements which had created these massive dislocations of the earth's crust, all taking place, in geological terms, in a relatively short time.

He also examines, in some detail, the effect of mineralisation along the lines of faulting, resulting in the rich veins of galena around Grassington, Kettlewell, Greenhow and in Swaledale and calamine around Malham – all being mined and smelted when he was writing. He also describes the small coalfields of Lonsdale and Ingleton, once part of the continuous coalfields of the Pennine basin, now preserved in the separate coalfields of Ingleton, North Lancashire, Stainmore and South Durham.

Chapter V **Physical Geography of the District** forms a key part of unravelling the structure of the Dales landscape. He begins by looking at the physical geography not just of the western Dales, but the whole of Yorkshire including the Millstone Grit and Coalfield areas of the old West Riding, as well as a description of the fascinating Magnesian

Giggleswick Scar on the western edge of the Craven Fault offers walkers magnificent view of Ribblesdale from its limestone pavements (author)

The characteristic flat topped gritstone summit of Pen-y-Ghent (694 metres), dominating "sweet and pastoral" Ribblesdale (author)

Limestone ridge which extends from south to north through the Vale of York.

Yet halfway through this very technical chapter describing sandstones, limestone, coal beds and shales, comes a passage of lyrical prose:

> It is the mountain or metalliferous limestone which gives to the north western part of Yorkshire and to the district of Craven those marking and distinctive features, which powerfully interest the geologist and the topographer, and lend an indescribable charm to the many sweet and pastoral dales, which lie in the shadow of bold mountains, girt with green belts or steep precipices of limestone and crowned with ruinous summits of millstone grit ...

Phillips goes to some trouble to explain how the scouring power of water has created the distinctive landscapes of Lunesdale and the Greta valley. But what he observes in upper Swaledale, around Kisdon, causes him to think hard:

Kisdon (Kearton) Hill, Upper Swaledale, above the village of Keld. The hill has been isolated by glacial action, causing the River Swale to change course

> *the isolated mount of Kearsden (Kisdon) in the double valley above Muker, seems inexplicable unless on the supposition of the passage of a great body of water.*[7]

Phillips was tantalisingly close to the truth – ice, not water, largely created these spectacular landscape features. In examining the evolving and changing patterns of hydrology, stream and river drainage in the Dales, he puzzles that:

> *it must always appear strange that waters should have flowed across natural valleys and ridges, but they should have crossed in their courses many of the mountains of Cumberland and Westmorland, left their spoils on the limestone hills of Orton, in the red sandstone of Eden and on the summit of Stainmoor*[8]

– what we would now call glacial erratics. It took his friend Jean Agassiz to solve that problem only a few years later.

It was not until his **Rivers, Mountains and Sea Coast of Yorkshire** of 1853 that Phillips speaks a little reluctantly of " – *the glacial drift of modern geologists*" and offers a section on "*The Glacial Period*" when he suggests areas like the Vale of Pickering were carved out "*aided perhaps by glaciers on the land and icebergs in the sea.*"[9]

In the last section of Chapter V Phillips moves from the physical description of the landscape, to deal rather grandly, with **Scenery**. As

Erratic rock near
Settle – sketch by
John Phillips

ERRATIC BLOCK NEAR SETTLE.

Phillips argues, the geologist can appreciate aesthetic qualities in a
landscape every bit as much as the artist. The two ways of seeing are not
in conflict:

> *Is the charm of fine scenery diminished because the secret
> agencies which have concurred in its production have become
> familiar to the reasoning geologist? Surely, he of all men should
> be most affected by the charms of nature ...?*[10]

What follows is a fulsome description of the essence of the Pennine
landscape – the green "conical" greywacke summits of the Howgill Fells,
dramatic waterfalls such as Cautley Spout, the immense North Pennines
escarpment from Hartside to Brough, *"one of the grandest features in
English geography"*, and the *"peculiar grandeur"* of the limestone scars
along the southern edge of the Dales between Ingleton and Kettlewell, as
well as the caves. He gives a fine description (and scientific explanation)
of the characteristic stepped shapes of the Yoredale summits which create
such distinctive and characteristic landscape features of the Yorkshire
Dales:

> *At the top of the series, under the rounded or angular craggy
> top of the millstone grit, and perhaps a small edge of chert or
> little limestone, the main or twelve fathom limestone will project
> a bold perpendicular scar; below it will be a little conclave
> or flat slope terminated by a second and less conspicuous*

*projection of the thinner underset limestone; a long slope
succeeds, simply or slightly varying with rising undulations
corresponding to the hard gritstones interstratified with shales;
this ends above a single or double scar of the middle limestone
conspicuous where thick, as in Addleburgh and Pen Hill, but
easily lost by the detritus of the superior rocks where it is thin,
as above Hawes; below this is another slope to the Simonside
(Simonstone) limestone, which forms a smooth terrace;
another steep slope to the Hardraw Scar limestone which runs
for miles along both sides of Wensleydale in a remarkable
terrace, occasionally woody, always very abrupt and based on a
steep slope of plates leading to the broad floor of the limestone
series.*[11]

He also goes on to describe some of the more interesting caves known
at that time, and their formation. This included Yordas and Weathercote

Hardraw Force
(author)

Caves, Hurtle Pot, Gowden Pot (Nidderdale), the "cavern" on Greenhow Hill (later known as Stump Cross) and one in Claphamdale which he was soon to visit with his friend James Farrer and which we now know as Ingleborough Cave. In particular he records how underground streams and carbonic acid in rainwater percolating through soils have contributed to carving out their distinctive formations, and the growth of their fascinating stalactites and stalagmites.

In the same chapter, again in lyrical flow, he comments:

> it is difficult to resist the desire of describing some of the ornaments of Yorkshire scenery; for nothing can be conceived more delightful to a tired wanderer on the mountains, after a long day's hammering, drawing, and measuring than to rest at the foot of the lofty cascade of Hardraw (96 feet) or listen to the everlasting murmur of the broken streams and woods of Cotter Force (See Turner's beautiful drawings of these fine waterfalls).[12]

Typically, he cannot resist giving the reader the exact height of the falls. He then goes on to a scientific description of how the typical waterfalls of the Dales such as Aysgarth, Hardraw, Mossdale or Mill Gill were created, and how their appearance and character are a result of the relative hardness or softness of the strata across and through which their streams flow.

Chapter VI **General Views** is back to a more prosaic and scientific description of how the sedimentary rocks of the Yorkshire Dales were laid down, with their characteristic organic remains, and explanation of how the mountain areas were elevated over aeons of time. Chapter VII **Description of the Fossils** is an extensive and detailed list and description of fossil types. He notes where they were discovered and recorded, many by Phillips himself, all arranged zoologically. These are illustrated by 22 fine plates superbly drawn by Phillips himself and engraved by J.W.Lowry.

Printed in York by Thomas Wilson & Sons of High Ousegate but now published by John Murray of London, the book was extremely well received and did much to further enhance his reputation as one of

The Howgill Fells (Andy Howard)

View along Dentdale towards Middleton Fell and Barbondale, looking across the line of the Pennine Fault (author)

the leading scientific minds of his generation. As well as subscribers' copies, fifty were dispatched to London to be sold in bookshops via John Murray. John Phillips with some justification was later to describe **Illustrations ... The Mountain Limestone District** as his best book, but it was one which had demanded huge intellectual effort from him.

Sadly, there were some quibbles from two of his close friends and fellow workers. Adam Sedgwick – notoriously slow to publish his own work – though he admired the book, and despite Philips's generous dedication to Sedgwick and to Vernon Harcourt, felt Phillips had trespassed on his own key areas of research along the great Pennine Fault that cuts across Dentdale, and geologically divides the Yorkshire Dales from the Lake District. This included a paper published by Sedgwick in 1835[13] that Sedgwick felt had not been properly acknowledged by Phillips (for which Phillips excused himself by pleading lack of time). Murchison grumbled about lack of maps and always sensitive about what he claimed to be his territory, suggested Phillips had not sufficiently acknowledged his own nomenclature of Silurian rocks.

But these were minor quibbles. **Illustrations of the Geology of Yorkshire – the Mountain Limestone District** remains a classic of nineteenth century scientific literature, a pivotal contribution to the understanding of the internationally important landscapes of the Yorkshire Dales.

Later authors, even if they have never read or even heard of John Phillips, have all been profoundly influenced by his insight into exactly what makes the landscape of the Yorkshire Dales, including its limestone formations, so very special. It remained the definitive guide to the geology of the Yorkshire Dales for almost a century, until the

Glacial erratic boulder on limestone pavement, Ingleborough National Nature Reserve
(Dorian Speakman)

monumental **Geology of Yorkshire** by Percy Kendall and Herbert Wroot in 1924. Kendall and Wroot also describe **Illustrations … Mountain Limestone** as Phillips' greatest work, and proceed to quote extensively from it.[14]

What about the southern part of Yorkshire, including the mainly gritstone South Pennines and the Yorkshire Coalfield? Could there have been an Illustrations Volume Three? Jack Morrell has produced a very convincing explanation of why this didn't happen.[15]

Phillips' drawings of typical mountain limestone bivalve fossils from Illustrations Part 2, engraved by J.W. Lowry (Yorkshire Museum collection)

When Phillips' Leeds friend Edward George died in 1830, George's unpublished research on the Yorkshire Coalfield was sent to Phillips for possible publication but Phillips by that time was overwhelmed by other priorities. In 1837 three keen local geologists, Thomas Wilson, Henry Hartop, and the Reverend William Thorp met in Wakefield to set up a society devoted to geological and mechanical research. Wilson and Hartop were both involved in the iron and coal industries, whilst Thorp, who had a passion for the landscape and rocks of his local area, was the Curate of Womersley, a village near Pontefract. The idea was both a scientific and a practical one – to provide technical education to support the area's new manufacturing and extractive industries, especially coal mining, which was expanding at a rapid rate in that part of the county. They turned to John Phillips for advice. Phillips attended their first meeting and helped to formulate the initial objects of what was named the Geological and Polytechnic Society of the West Riding of Yorkshire (GPSWRY). This rather lengthy title was intended to suggest the new Society's involvement with practical matters of engineering as well as geology. In 1903 it became the more simple and memorable Yorkshire Geological Society.

Professor Percy Kendall, President of the Yorkshire Geological Society 1910–11 (British Geological Survey)

Though John Phillips and William Smith were made the Society's first Honorary Members, Phillips was not able to become heavily involved with the new body. As Morrell suggests, the highly complex rock structures of the Yorkshire Coalfield offered a lot less inspiration to Phillips than the scenically beautiful and uplifting landscapes of Yorkshire Dales. Phillips was also still closely linked to the rival Yorkshire Philosophical Society. But as Barbara Pyrah notes, whilst geology had been a major part of the work of the Yorkshire Philosophical Society in its early days, by the 1850s a mere four geological papers were presented to the YPS. This compared with around ten times that number given to the younger GPSWRY in the same period, including several papers by Phillips himself[16] as well as papers on mining and civil engineering, electricity, physics, agriculture, and the applied sciences.

William Thorp, who had become the first Honorary Secretary and later a Vice President of GPSWRY, even planned, in 1844 to write and publish an **Illustrations of the Geology of the Yorkshire Coal District** – in effect a Part Three to Phillips' two **Illustrations of the Geology of Yorkshire Part One** and **Part Two**, using the same format. Sadly there were not enough subscribers to allow this to be financially possible.[17] Thorp published some sections of what might have been the Coalfield project in 1847, but it was not until the 1860s that detailed surveys were done of the area by the Geological Survey. The Yorkshire Coalfield and the South Pennines were not to receive full and comprehensive coverage until Percy Kendall and Herbert Wroot's **Geology of Yorkshire**.

The GPSWRY, even though it lacked Phillips' direct involvement, continued to flourish. Under its shorter title The Yorkshire Geological Society, in the twentieth century the Society became the leading academic and professional body concerned with earth sciences in the region, with close links to Leeds, Sheffield and Newcastle Universities and to the Geological Survey. Its activities involved not just earth sciences in the industrial West Riding, but the whole of historic Yorkshire, extending into the coalfield areas of the North Midlands and as far north as Durham.

This is a role that continues to the present day. The Yorkshire Geological Society through its publications, lectures, seminars, and outreach activities, continues the achievements of its great Victorian founders, pushing the frontiers of geological science in the region, and communicating knowledge and enthusiasm for the science to new audiences and later generations of both professional and amateur scientists in ways that John Phillips would have thoroughly understood and approved.

Notes

1 Phillips John 1834: *Guide to Geology* London: Longmans Preface pxii

2 Phillips John 1836: *Illustrations of the Geology of Yorkshire* Vol 2 London: John Murray Preface xvi

3 Wordsworth William 1820 *Sonnets from the River Duddon:* Afterthought

4 *Ibid.* p15

5 *Ibid.* p36–37

6 *Ibid.* p135

7 *Ibid.* p156

8 *Ibid.* p162

9 Phillips John 1853 *The Rivers, Mountains and Sea Coast of Yorkshire* London: John Murray p90, p184

10 Phillips 1836 John *op. cit.* p164

11 *Ibid.* p168–9

12 *Ibid.* p171

13 Sedgwick Adam 1835: *Introduction to the general structure of the Cumbrian Mountains;* Transactions of the Geological Society of London 4 p47–48

14 Kendall PF and Wroot HE 1924: *Geology of Yorkshire* Leeds: Authors Vol 2 p835–836

15 Morrell Jack 2005 *John Phillips and the business of Victorian Science* Aldershot: Ashford pp170–171

16 Pyrah Barbara 1988: *The History of the Yorkshire Museum and its geological collections* York: Sessions pp77–78

17 Morrell Jack 2005 *op. cit.* p171.

Staithes harbour, developed around the "mouth of the little stream which gives life and picturesque beauty to Staithes" – John Phillips (Andy Howard)

6

Topographer, artist and popular writer

The Railway Revolution came to York on 29th May 1839 when the Yorkshire & North Midlands Railway under the Chairmanship of the notorious "Railway King" George Hudson connected York by rail to the recently opened Leeds and Selby Railway at Gascoigne Wood junction. By July 1840 there was a through express train service operating to London[1] taking a "mere" ten hours. The line from York to Scarborough was opened in 1845 and onto Filey and Bridlington in 1846, and to Hull via Seamer and Filey by 1848. Over this and the next two decades there was a frenzy of railway building, a period of financial boom and bust that was to change British society forever, leading to the opening up communications and the sharing of ideas in hitherto unimagined ways. It created huge new possibilities for someone like John Phillips whose lecturing career depended on being able to travel between the growing industrial cities and towns of England. He could also reach villages and hamlets deep in the countryside for his geological surveying and fossil hunting as branch lines were built. Newly dug railway cuttings, embankments and tunnels were a new rich source of material and knowledge for palaeontologists and geologists.

For John Phillips, at that time always looking for ways to augment his modest salary (the British Association were now paying him a still relatively modest salary of £300 per year), the newly opened railways gave him an opportunity to supplement his income by writing topographical guidebooks for a newly mobile, newly literate audience, eager to explore the places the new railways would take them.

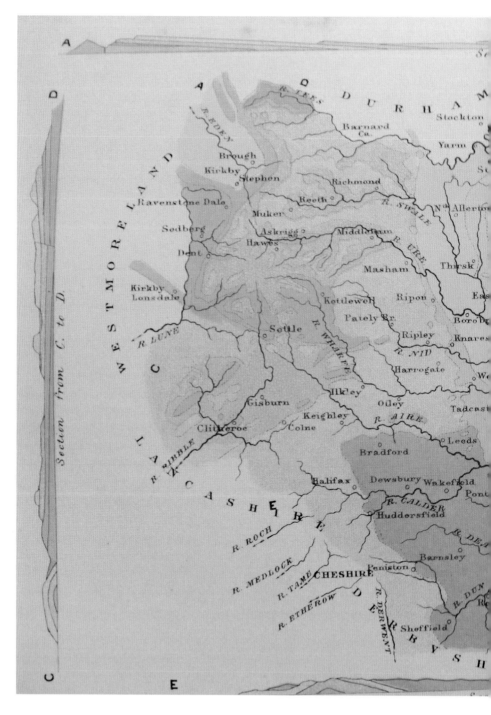

The pioneering 1853 printed map of Yorkshire from **The Rivers, Mountains and Sea Coast of Yorkshire**

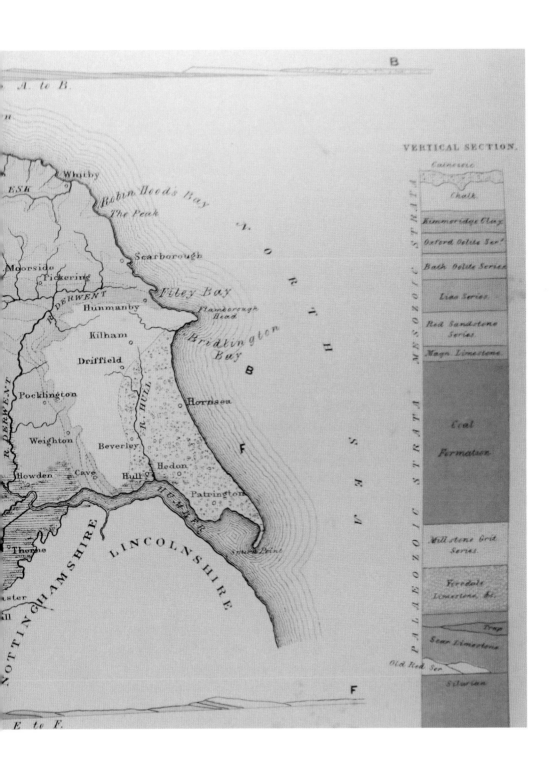

So despite his many commitments and workloads, in 1853 he produced **The Rivers, Mountains and Sea Coast of Yorkshire,** a guidebook to what he considered to be some of the most attractive landscape features and countryside of his adopted county. Though once again supported by pre-publication subscriptions, this book was also published by London publisher John Murray at a cost of ten shillings to subscribers or fifteen shillings from bookshops. This made it a publication very much targeted at better off, sophisticated middle-class readers.

Rivers, Mountains and Sea-Coast of Yorkshire is arguably one of the best books ever written about the landscape of Yorkshire.

As he suggested in the Preface:

> *There exists, I believe, nothing in print, which professes to do what is here attempted: to win from the hasty traveller an hour's delay at the station, a day's wandering by the waterfalls, a week's ramble over rocky hills.*[2]

There had been many local guides to specific attractions such as Fountains Abbey or local caves, or to towns such as Whitby or Scarborough. And there were plenty of guidebooks from Leland and Celia Fiennes onwards describing journeys through the county.

However, unlike typical later Victorian and early Edwardian Railway Guide book writers such as Bevan in his **Tourist Guide to the East and North Ridings of Yorkshire** (1887)[3] or Baddeley, who even printed railway timetables and charabanc departures as well as details of hotels and golf courses in his **Thorough Guide Series**[4] **Yorkshire Parts 1 and 2** (1909), Phillips was not attempting to give a complete blow-by-blow taxonomy of Yorkshire. His was a personal choice of destinations including many of the places he had over the previous 30 years walked or travelled to by carriage with his uncle, with friends and on his own, but which were now accessible by train. As in all guidebooks, some areas are dealt with adequately but fairly superficially, but the areas such as his favourite Craven limestone uplands, Dales, Moors, and the Yorkshire coastline get far more attention.

But in some ways it is a curious book: part scientific handbook to the county with lists of statistics of the height of hills, rainfall, land mass

Buttertubs Pass, between Upper Swaledale and Wensleydale (John Carey)

and rainwater catchment, the habit of a scientist with a passion for information gathering and classification. Yet there are also passages of lyrical prose, and beautiful observation of the natural world, of the effect of light on landscape or historic features.

The book opens with an epic sweep describing Yorkshire as *"once the home of the most powerful English tribe and now the largest English county"*, before defining the county through its river systems, and the constant process of erosion from rainfall, streams and rivers shaping the landscape we see today:

> *The mere action of the humid and variable atmosphere of England is wasting, every hour, the surfaces of what are thought to be eternal hills*[5]

It is carefully structured. In the opening chapter on "Principal Features of Physical Geography", he looks in turn at the mountains, rivers and coasts of the title, then offers a scholarly section on Yorkshire's climate, followed by a curious short chapter on Magnetism (magnetic polar variation). Then follows a lengthier summary on Yorkshire Geology,

Flora and Fauna, and three chapters on early human history – The Brigantes (for Phillips a generic term for Stone, Bronze and Iron Age/Celtic cultures), Anglo Saxons and Danes and finally Romans. Appendices follow with more lists of all hill summits, an essay on stalagmites, water quality, coastal erosion, and details of a Roman fortress and battle sites.

In the Chapter on "Mountains" which we would nowadays refer to as "Fells", the areas of north west Yorkshire that Phillips knew and loved are described not just with lists of prosaic facts such as their heights and rock structures, but with a warmth of feeling only experienced by someone who has walked if not all, then most of them. He knows which summits are worth an ascent but also those which are "uninviting" or even have a "dreary magnificence". As he points out (of course in days before motor traffic):

> *Though it is hardly worth the trouble to climb Shunnor Fell, or Lovely Seat, the road that runs between them from Muker to Hawes should be followed by every pedestrian who enjoys the mountain air and can appreciate wild and striking combinations of moorland summits. This pass is called "Buttertubs" and should by no means be taken in the contrary direction to what is here recommended. The evening views onwards to the south on gaining the summit, is of the utmost grandeur – Ingleborough, Whernside and other fine outlines, coming boldly out beyond the broad undulations about the head of Yoredale.[6]*

No other writer of his time gives such exact, geological detail, explaining how the rocks or land formations he is looking at have shaped the landscape. The walker to the summit of Ingleborough, an "easy" morning walk when he lived with Smith at Kirkby Lonsdale, is offered a detailed description of the hut circles, within what at that time was believed to be a walled hill fort.

Caves, their formation, palaeontology and archaeology were a lifetime fascination for Phillips and he lists several of the better known caves and potholes in the vicinity – Gingle Pot, Hurtle Pot, Weathercote Cave, Douk Hole, Gauber and Gatekirk Caves. There is a fine description of

Natural limestone formations inside Ingleborough Cave (© Ingleborough Cave)

Ingleborough Cave,[7] first discovered in 1837, which is largely based on the research of his friend, local landowner and intrepid cave explorer James Farrer, who pioneered the way into the subterranean caverns by swimming through a deep pool, attached to his waiting companions by a rope, reputedly lighting his way with a candle attached to his cap. Phillips goes into greater detail on the physical and chemical processes of cavern and stalactite formation and correctly suggests how its underground stream must have originated in Little Beck and the mighty Gaping Gill waterfall, which later speleological research has confirmed.

What is now known as the Forest of Bowland (now largely in Lancashire) and the South Pennines however receive relatively superficial treatment, and even the Moors and Wolds are in this section mainly a list of summits and generalisations about the shape of land features.

The rivers and their valleys – or Dales – form the core of the topographical sections of the book – the Tees, Lune, Ribble and Eden in the north and west and then the whole series of great rivers that feed south and eastwards into the Humber which as he notes takes 80% of the waters of Yorkshire – from the rivers Esk, Derwent, Ure, Wharfe, Aire, Calder, Nidd, Don and Hull.

Kirkstall Abbey, Leeds in its still-wooded Airedale setting (Dorian Speakman)

The more attractive and historic towns, cities and antiquities on the banks of the principal rivers also receive attention in what is, after all, a guide for visitors, but the industrial areas are less well covered.

The city of Hull receives good coverage and Doncaster on the Don is deemed "one of the prettiest towns in the north of England." However Wakefield gets scarcely a mention, whilst neither Sheffield, Halifax, Huddersfield nor Bradford have any reference (not being on significant rivers being a reason). Leeds has a somewhat equivocal description. Comparing what this part of Airedale and Kirkstall Abbey would have looked like in the twelfth century, he notes:

> *Then, from the high rocks Malham and the pastures of Craven to Loidis in Elmet, the deer, wild boar and white bull were wandering in unfrequented woods, or wading in untainted waters or wandering over boundless heaths. Now hundreds of men of many races have extirpated the wood, dyed the water with tints derived from other lands, turned the heaths into fertile fields and*

filled the valley with mills and looms, water wheels and engine chimneys. Yet not all the beauty of Airedale is lost; nor would the thoughtful mind which now regards the busy stream of the Aire, lament the change. The quiet spinner is happier than the rude and violent hunter, the spirit of true religion fills these populous villages as well as once it filled those cloistered walls; the woods are gone, and in their place the iron road; but that road conducts the intelligent lover of beauty to other hills and dales where art has had no contest with nature ...[8]

Even York, his adopted home town, whose history and special qualities he details with affection, had suffered from development, including the railway, which in recent years had:

not effaced, but much impaired its antique and singular character. The ramparts reared over Saxon walls and Roman villas open to admit Stevenson and his chariots alike impressed with the stamp of the latest iron age; railway stations replace

Drawing of York's original station inside the city walls dating from the 1860s, showing the extent to which the new railway breached the city's ancient walls.

the abbeys and hospitals which sheltered within the walls; the
castle is transformed into a jail; the Gothic bridge is gone; the
very river has lost the tide; and we can hardly trace the ford or
ferry by which the soldiers crossed the camp of Eburacum to
enjoy the bath on the road to Calcaria.[9]

However it is the wilder and remoter parts of Yorkshire that most excite
the imagination of Phillips. In describing a favourite hike in Ease Gill,
between Kingsdale and Barbondale, immediately below Great Coum and
a location still unknown to most walkers, his skills as geologist, naturalist
and writer combine:

In dry seasons the challenge of the stream which descends
from Great Colne (Great Coum) and Gregarth to Leck and
Over-Burrow to join the Lune, is a wild hollow of stones;
in wet seasons these are rolled along by a powerful torrent.
In ascending the stream we find not only its actual banks,
but considerable hills on its sides to be composed of similar
materials, drifted together by some earlier forces of water.
Farther upwards these pebble-banks give place to the native
slaty rock, which has been their prolific parent, and the little
stream winds, falls, and rushes through these rocks with a great
variety of beautiful and intricate scenery. On a small scale it is
indeed admirable, especially when reduced by long continued

Easegill (Walking Englishman)

*drought to the pure and perpetual feeders which are its proper
source. The water is then of a clear and beautiful green and is
collected in little fairy pools or pouring in tiny cascades over
the blue, slaty rocks which it has sculptured and perforated in a
thousand ways. Hazel, holly, ivy, mountain ash, and a hundred
other humbler plants, combine with the heathy ground and
lichen-grey rocks into minutely beautiful pictures.*[10]

Or when describing the River Esk approaching Glaisdale in the Moors,
Phillips can bring the feeling of artist or poet to the observational
precision of the scientist:

*The river is in fact barred from a direct course by cross ridges
of sandstone and shale, through which its deep and winding
channel is cut. Through the woods which cover the greater part
of the surface the shale peeps out in high dark cliffs, and here
and there white crags of gritstone appear on the edge. Often
too they lie in huge confusion on the slopes, or make islands in
the water, and serve with fallen trees for cheap and primitive
bridges. Not a house in this wild, sylvan scene nor a sound
save that of the swift Esk breaking into a thousand falls, and
running by its own sweet will in many little streams. In autumn
the rich hues of decaying foliage are charmingly lit up by the
fresh green leaves and bright red berries of the holly.*[11]

Winter sunshine on River Esk, Glaisdale (author)

Rudston Monolith, in the churchyard, Rudston (author)

Not surprisingly, many of the finest sections of the book are those when the geologist sees both the structure and the detail of the landscape. Phillips often recommends the reader to take a particular short walk along a path or section of cliff such as Staintondale Cliff north of Scarborough or near Staithes.

In writing about the Yorkshire Wolds, Phillips gives a detailed description of the Gypsey Race, the constantly vanishing stream that runs below and occasionally above the chalk through The Great Wold Valley in the northern Wolds. He was one of the first to note that the stone of Rudston monolith came from the coast several miles away to the north – as we now know probably from Cayton Bay[12] near Scarborough.

As well as the natural history, geology and geomorphology, it is the county's rich antiquarian or archaeological heritage that fills much of the book. As the former Keeper to the Yorkshire Museum, Phillips was well aware of the rich archaeological heritage of the county. This is typified by the many tumuli and cairns on the summit ridges of both the North York Moors and the Wolds. He describes a walk across the Moors with his friend Jonathan Gray in 1836 in the company of a large group of local country people to inspect and "open" some of the mounds on the moorland between Kirkbymoorside and Ingilby – and of finding a fine ancient urn in so doing,[13] but probably disturbing the sites in ways that would make modern archaeologists maybe howl in despair.

There is a beautiful description of the Anglo-Saxon sundial at St Gregory's Minster in Kirkdale, Kirkbymoorside, with translations of the carved text.[14] There are frequent references to recent local archaeological finds in every area he describes. He is also one of the first Yorkshire authors to continually refer back to the meaning of place names to establish the nature of early settlement – whether British (Celtic), Saxon or Viking. He had a remarkable knowledge both of prehistoric trackways such as Wold Gate across the Wold summits between York and Bridlington, and the network of Roman roads across the county, which as he notes frequently mark ancient parish boundaries.

 For the modern reader it is often the simple, telling detail that brings the descriptions to life – such as the fact that waggonette parties from Whitby used to travel up to Goathland, Glaisdale and Egton Bridge in days before the railway. He notes how the new railway connection between Scarborough and Whitby via Malton and Pickering actually reduced access to Robin Hood's Bay for a time when the direct stagecoach between the two main towns was withdrawn:

> *But Robin Hood's Bay is now even more difficult of access,*
> *except to pedestrians, than formerly as the railway has stopped*
> *the primitive coach which used to drag its slow length between*

Kirkdale Minster. The Anglo-Saxon sundial is just inside the porch (author)

Scarborough and Whitby, and thus at least approach the Peak and Bay Town. For bold pedestrians however, there can hardly be a pleasanter walk from along the cliffs from Whitby or Scarborough to Robin Hood's Bay.[15]

The direct coastal railway between Scarborough and Whitby via Robin Hood's Bay was only opened in 1885 and sadly closed 80 years later – it is now ironically a popular footpath and cycleway.

The latter part of the book follows a set of 25 lithographed plates using exquisitely drawn sketches by Phillips of popular Yorkshire landscape or heritage features, in a style very much in the manner of his hero J.M.W. Turner and lithographed by William Monkhouse of York. They include the waterfalls at Aysgarth, Thornton, Mill Gill, Hardraw, Gayle, Weathercote, and High Force, as well as drawings of such iconic and popular features as Brimham Rocks, Kilnsey Crag, Buttertubs Pass, Ilkley's Cow and Calf rocks, Gordale Scar, Malham Cove, Roseberry Topping, Barnard Castle, the view from Wharncliffe Lodge near Sheffield. There are drawings of the sections of the coast he knew so

Bay Town, Robin Hood's Bay (Dorian Speakman)

Brimham Rocks, Nidderdale
drawing by John Phillips

well – rocks at Flamborough, Filey Brigg, the coastal bays (complete with carefully positioned human figures in top hat or crinoline) at Scarborough, Runswick Bay, Robin Hood's Bay, Staithes, Rockcliffe. In addition there are sketches of Ilkley's Anglo Viking Crosses, a section of Ingleborough Cave, plans of Roman forts, maps showing "Brigante" settlements.

Each Plate has a separate short piece of descriptive text which refers back to the main body of text. For example he describes Thornton Force near Ingleton:

Thornton Force by John Phillips. The summit of Whernside is just visible in the background

This place will please the geologist quite as much as the artist. In ascending from the Force, by Yorda's Cave, to the summit of Whernside, the whole series of Mountain Limestone is crossed, and on top of the mountain is the Millstone Grit.

Or as he writes about the fine panoramic view of Scarborough's South Bay (Plate XXVI):

The visitor of the seaside who merely walks on the sands, or rides on the roads, will have but a slight notion of the many picturesque combinations of land and sea which reward those who tread the margin of the cliffs. I affirm that half the beauty and grandeur of our coast is lost to those who follow merely the beaten tracks.[16]

That "margin of the cliffs" or cliff top path we now know as The Cleveland Way.

Of special interest is a beautifully drawn and coloured geological map of Yorkshire, an updated version of his uncle's. However this was printed,

Scarborough from cliff top (John Philips)

Topographer, artist and popular writer

not hand coloured, using a technique known as chromolithography, making this one of the world's first colour printed geological maps. Ever alert to the possibilities offered by new technologies, and aware of new commercial opportunities, Phillips also published a larger version of the map, 22 x 20 inches, selling at 7 shillings flat or 10 shillings mounted.[17]

Following the success of **Rivers, Mountains and Sea Coasts**, Phillips was quick to recognise that there was now a gap in the market for a very much cheaper, handier pocket-sized guidebook for a new generation of lower middle and working class travellers on the recently opened steam railway. Within a few weeks of publishing **Rivers Mountains and Sea Coasts** in 1853, it was in the bookshops (WH Smith had opened their first station bookshop in Euston in 1848). It was self-published by Phillips himself, and printed by Goddard and Lancaster who were based in both Hull and York. Entitled **Railway Excursions from York, Leeds and Hull**, it was divided as suggested in its title into three sections – Excursions from York, Hull and Leeds respectively. It was rapidly reprinted in 1854 and 1855, this last edition now published by John Sampson of Coney Street, York with the title **Professor Phillips's Railway Excursions in Yorkshire by the North Eastern Railway**) and priced at one shilling for sale at the new railway bookstalls. This new title was timely, clearly aimed at travellers on the newly established Northern Eastern Railway, created by an amalgamation in 1854 of several smaller local railway companies.

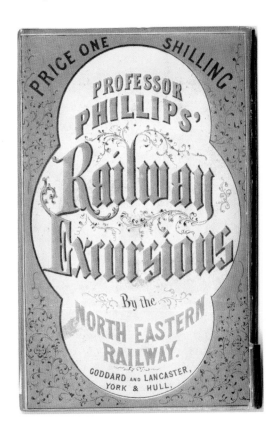

Cover of the John Phillips' popular guidebook **Excursions from the North Eastern Railway** (from the collection of Oxford University Museum; image courtesy of the Museum)

Railway Excursions had the clear intention of showing travellers – including "southrons" from London, the:

> *easiest way of reaching many of the most interesting points of scenery and remarkable objects of antiquity; by easy deviations from the railways which now traverse this district in many directions, and invite the children of toil and the denizens of town to short excursion among the hill and waterfalls.*[18]

With the possible exception of the 1836 Belcher and Dodgson's rather refined illustrated guide to the horse-drawn Whitby and Pickering Railway,[19] **Railway Excursions** is one of the world's first railway tourist guidebooks. It was aimed at visitors coming to explore Yorkshire's heritage by the new train services, but also at day trippers from the rapidly growing industrial towns and cities of Yorkshire now able to explore for the first time the dales, moors, historic towns and coast of their native county. Written in a more popular style than **Rivers, Mountains and Sea Coast**, the guidebook offers not only insights of what can be seen from the train carriage window, including interesting historical sights a short walk from a particular railway station, but it also suggests more extended walks from those stations into the local countryside. Who else but Phillips would suggest, in the waiting time when changing at Seamer from York on a journey from York to Filey, Bridlington or Hull (which rail travellers still have to do to this day), what interesting geology is to be observed close to the station platforms in a nearby local quarry?[20]

The Tower of Richmond Castle: illustration from **Excursions from the North Eastern Railway**

Swaledale – which he first visited with his uncle in 1819 on a trip to the Auld Gang lead mine above Reeth[21] – had long been a passion for Phillips and he devotes no less than ten pages of text to Swaledale itself, including an enchanting description of Easby Abbey and Richmond, a town which after describing an evening walk under *soft blue shades and under golden clouds* he describes as *the most romantic town in England*.

His regret is that there is no *Reeth and Swaledale 'Bus* from Richmond to Upper Swaledale, a defect he hopes the Railway Company will supply in the summer months with a suitable service:

> which is so much to be lamented, as shutting out one of the most beautiful tracts in the country from all but individuals with strong limbs or long purses.

– no doubt the first ever plea for better public transport to allow people to access and enjoy the matchless landscapes of what is now a National Park. But once he has walked deep into the dale, the sheer joy of being in such a beautiful landscape comes through the description of lovely section of wooded valley at Marske, five miles from Richmond station on the long-vanished Darlington-Richmond branch railway:

> I am writing this near a small farmhouse and some fine trees, which lend themselves to every mood of the sky; the sycamores, with the rocks on the hill above them, stand well for a storm; the ashes and elms, looking down on the river, suit a milder heaven, and are in keeping with the glancing lights and shades so common in midday in this elevated region, still more in harmony with the softer tints and broader shades of evening.[22]

Higher up the Dale, amongst some of the wildest moorlands in Britain he warns his readers:

> But all to whom solitude is distasteful, all for whom luxurious accommodation has charms, are more than warned against more than a glance at the stern aspect of Upper Swaledale.

All the obvious main tourist attractions accessible by the new railway lines are described, including the great abbeys and castles, as well as celebrated landscape features such as Roseberry Topping, Flamborough

View of wooded hillsides near the village of Marske, Swaledale (author)

Head and Hackfall Woods. He features all the well-known heritage towns and cities now on the rail network, starting with the many treasures of York – which has an extended reference not surprisingly to the Yorkshire Museum and its Gardens – but also Scarborough, Whitby, Beverley, Bridlington, Ripon, Malton. All have references to key attractions easily reached from their railway stations. At every opportunity, the observations of a sharp-eyed geologist are there to explain and interpret what is there to be seen:

> *The geological structure of the hilly west of Harrogate is remarkable – framed on an anticline and syncline axes, indicative of great internal disturbances. It is along this line of movement that the mineral sources are found. Some of their peculiarities are referred to the boggy surface soil, but we believe salt impregnation, which is the basis of the sulphur waters, is due to deeper subterranean solutions.*[23]

An especially fascinating aspect of the **Excursions** for modern readers is that the book takes the traveller along several now long closed branch railways. By 1853 many of these had been recently opened to allow ordinary people to reach parts of the county hitherto difficult or impossible for all but the most affluent people in society to access. Phillips describes a trip on the now long-forgotten meandering railway line between Malton, Hovingham and Coxwold (for Byland Abbey) only just opened in 1853 and closed a century later. A lovely description of the equally long closed Malton-Driffield railway through the Yorkshire Wolds turns into a geology lesson:

> we continue in the chalk country, with frequent deep cuttings to the complicated system of hollows, terminating in Burdale tunnel. The dale leading to this costly work is a good example of a wold valley, dry, or nearly so, at all times, with gently rounded sides, excavated by water no doubt, but not by water derived from rain or springs. It is the work of the ancient sea.
>
> In the long tunnel which now receives us, the chalk was fairly cut through, and the subsequent clay was penetrated. This clay, slippery with the water which passed down to it from the chalk above, caused much trouble and expense, breaking the woodwork and disordering the arching. On emerging from the gloomy passage, we glide through the narrow valley in the Kimmeridge clay, by the station for Wharram, cut through the oolitic rock opposite Settrington, enter the broad vale of Pickering at its southwestern extremity, and arrive at Malton.[24]

Northern (Wharram Percy) entrance to Burdale Tunnel on the former Malton-Driffield Railway line (Yorkshire Wolds Railway ©Mrs Wray)

Another memorable journey is between Malton and Whitby on the former Whitby and Pickering Railway, now preserved in part as the North Yorkshire Moors steam heritage line. There is a rare description of Goathland railway incline in use, with its stationary engine, closed and replaced by a less steep divisionary loop more suitable for conventional steam locomotives in 1865. When Phillips was travelling in the early 1850s the locomotive was detached and:

> *The descent of this long and rather sinuous inclined plane is accomplished very safely by the aid of machinery, which is urged by steam and controlled by the engineer.*

Among walks suggested from Goathland's old station is one to the lovely waterfall of Thomason Force or the prehistoric hut circles on Goathland Moor. And Phillips doesn't hesitate to remind geologists to alight at "Tunnel" (Beckhole) Station to view a "singular dyke" and ironstone beds, *"which here are intermingled with the lias"*.

A steam train on the North York Moors Railway through the glacial valley of Newtondale (author)

Topographer, artist and popular writer

Thomason Foss (author)

These are typical of the kind of detail offered by Phillips in **Excursions** which provide a remarkable record of early rail travel, of equal interest to the railway historian and to those who appreciate descriptions of the Yorkshire landscape as it was in the mid-nineteenth century.

Yet on the train journey from Milford into Leeds the description takes a somewhat different tone:

Mill workers at Marshall's Flax Mill Leeds (from **The Story of English Towns, Leeds** J.S. Fletcher 1912)

[Interior of Marshall's Flax-Mill.]

Here the atmosphere changes – we quit the green meadows
and the pleasant or splendid abodes, the reward of honourable
industry, and enter the darker shadows of the engines and
workshops, where that industry is unceasing. Let Whitaker (a
popular nineteenth-century topographer who dealt mainly
with country estates and aristocratic lineage) *declaim as he*
will against mills and looms, we who live in Yorkshire know too
well their value in augmenting the comforts of the people to join
in the rude and thankless cry. Rather let us attend a meeting
of the Institute, or the Philosophical Society, and learn how
earnest a love of literature, science and art is fostered under this
dingy atmosphere; let us enter the factory, and, with unselfish
sympathy, invite the hardworking children of the West Riding to
accompany us on a railway excursion.[25]

One delightful touch in the **Excursions** are the advertisements in the
rear pages for Phillips' own publications including his **Geological Map
of Yorkshire** and **Rivers, Mountains and Sea Coast of Yorkshire** which
as he astutely indicates:

This new edition being limited in numbers, persons desirous of
obtaining it, are requested to apply to the Author (St Mary's
Lodge, York) – price to subscribers 10 shillings. The price will be
raised on the day of publication.

In 1854 John Phillips' appointment as Deputy Reader in Geology at
Oxford University took precedence over his literary activities.

Rivers, Mountains and Sea Coast (reprinted in 1855) was a hugely
influential book. Few writers on the Yorkshire landscape have not
been directly or indirectly influenced by his erudition and scholarship.
Even where new research has dated Phillips' science, the writer's genial
personality and insight remains an attraction.

Railway Excursions was soon to spawn many imitations, including a
whole tradition of railway-based geological field guides of which Kendall
& Wroots' **Geology of Yorkshire** is perhaps the most eminent – **Volume
2** – is entirely devoted to field trips using Yorkshire's once extensive rail
network.

But above all is a recognition that John Phillips was one of the pioneering interpreters of the Yorkshire landscape, especially of the northern, western and coastal parts of the county.

As an energetic rambler, few writers before or since have covered so many miles on foot, or had such an intimate yet scientific knowledge of the Yorkshire Coast, Moors, Dales and Wolds. Few have written about these areas with such eloquence combined with a scientific understanding. This makes John Phillips one of the earliest but also most successful and influential Yorkshire walker-writers of all time.

In his later years he walked less out of necessity (though he had done a good deal of that in his earlier years) but for the simple physical pleasure of the activity. For John Phillips a journey on foot released an infinite curiosity in what lay beyond the road or footpath, as much as when he watched the world pass by from a railway carriage window.

In so many respects, his enthusiasm and passion for those special landscapes, passed on to and shared by his readers, were for his own and later generations a continuing inspiring force which directly led to the creation of our two great National Parks – the Yorkshire Dales and the North York Moors – as well as Yorkshire's Heritage Coast and three Areas of Outstanding Natural Beauty.

Notes

1 Peacock SA.J. and Joy David 1971: *George Hudson of York* Clapham, North Yorkshife: Dalesman p24

2 Phillips John 1853 *Rivers, Mountains and Sea-Coast of Yorkshire* London: John Murray p. viii

3 Bevan G. Phillips 1887 Tourist Guide to the East and North Ridings of Yorkshire London: Edward Stanford

4 Baddeley MJB 1906 Thorough Guide Series (Yorkshire Part 1 &) 2 London: Thomas Nelson pp i–vii

5 Phillips John 1853 Op. Cit p12

6 *Ibid.* p21

7 *Ibid.* p27–8

8 *Ibid.* p94.

9 *Ibid.* p73–4

10 *Ibid.* p115

11 *Ibid.* p108

12 *Ibid.* p106

13 *Ibid.* 10

14 *Ibid.* p87–8

15 *Ibid.* p136–7

16 Phillips John 1853 Op. Cit p287–8

17 Morrell Jack 2005 *John Phillips and the Business of Victorian Science* Aldershot: Ashgate p327–8

18 Phillips John 1854 Railway Excursions from York, Leeds and Hull (2nd edition) p3

19 Belcher, H.; Dodgson, G. 1836 *in the north eastern part of Yorkshire"* London: Longmans

20 Philip *op. cit.* 1854 p42

21 Philips John 1844 *op. cit.* p88

22 Phillips John 1854 *op. cit.* p24

23 Phillips John 1854 *ibid.* p72

24 *Ibid.* p57

25 *Ibid.* p68

Warrendale Knotts near Victoria Cave, Settle. Phillips' classic "Mountain Limestone" karst landscape and a feature he would have seen on his last visit to the Yorkshire Dales in September 1873 (Dorian Speakman)

7
Absence – and return to Yorkshire

In September 1853, on his way back from the British Association
meeting in Hull, Henry Strickland, FRS, Deputy Reader in Geology at
Oxford, chose to spend a little time examining some interesting exposed
strata on the lineside, in a cutting on the newly built Manchester Sheffield
and Lincolnshire Railway near Retford. Seeing a goods trains approach
on the twin track line, he stepped backwards on to the other track to
avoid it, only to be hit and killed by a fast approaching passenger train
coming from the other direction.[1]

That tragedy was to have a huge impact on the life of John Phillips. Barely
fifteen days after the accident, he was approached by the University
authorities and offered Strickland's post. The haste in making the
appointment was largely owing to the fact that with the continuing
illness, mental and physical, of the Reader in Geology, Professor William
Buckland, the University faced a crisis. Such was the urgent need to get
someone in place for the teaching and lecturing tasks that needed to be
done that the University agreed to appoint someone to the prestigious
post who was not only not an Oxford man, but not even a University
graduate.

This anomaly was soon put right with a hastily arranged award of a
Master's degree within days of Phillips' arrival in the University.

In reality the University was highly fortunate, given the fact that at
that time John Phillips happened to be available and was surviving on
relatively modest income. Having concluded his work for the Yorkshire

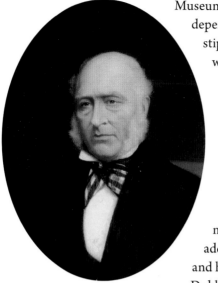

Museum and the Geological Survey, he was dependent on just his British Association stipend, and a modest income from his writing, lecturing and publications.

He already had a formidable record as one of the intellectual giants of nineteenth century science, not just in the sister disciplines of geology and palaeontology, but in several other fields. His many major publications, including two academic textbooks on geology, were for many years, standard works of reference. In addition there was his reputation as a lecturer and his former Chairs in both London and Dublin, his Fellowship of the Royal Society, and his 1845 Wollaston Medal, This made him the obvious and unrivalled candidate for a post of national importance. It was the breakthrough John Phillips richly deserved.

Through the offices of his friend Professor Charles Daubeney, the post came with an offer of attractive free accommodation – a cottage for Anne and himself, in central Oxford, close to Magdalen Bridge. Financial security together with the many opportunities available for an academic in one of Europe's leading universities, made it too great an opportunity for someone of Phillips' talent and ambition to miss.

But unlike the Chairs in London and Dublin, which had been more like visiting professorships, the Oxford post demanded his full-time presence and attendance. Leaving York and Yorkshire was inevitably a sad necessity for both John and Anne. Their home at St Mary's Lodge was retained as a *pied-a-terre* and source of rented sub-let income (an advertisement was placed in the local press for a suitable sub-tenant). Phillips didn't give up the lease until 1870. As he was to recall in 1866,

> *the great county, in which thirty thoughtful years were afterwards passed, became known to me as probably to no others.*[2]

But Oxford and its great University offered major new possibilities. The next two decades saw Phillips consolidate his position as one of the leading national figures of progressive Victorian science. He became Reader in Geology at the University after Buckland's death in 1856, in 1858–60 served as the President of the prestigious Geological Society of London and finally, in 1860, was given the full title of Professor at Oxford.

As well as his teaching and lecturing duties, his many Museum curatorial skills were also to prove invaluable. He was appointed Keeper of the famous Ashmolean Museum in Oxford from 1856–70 and, what was to be one of his greatest achievements, he helped to conceive, design and create the nationally important Oxford Natural History Museum. He became its Keeper from 1857 until his death in 1874.

His regular Oxford public lectures on a wide range of different scientific topics drew large audiences. From the mid-1860s these were also open to ladies who at that time were not allowed to take degrees. On many occasions, women, thirsty for knowledge and opportunities denied to them elsewhere formed the larger part of the audience.

Oxford Museum of Natural History taken about the time of its opening in 1860 (© Oxford University Museum)

A rare visit back to Yorkshire was made to Leeds in 1858 on the occasion of the British Association for the Advancement of Science meeting in the city. Phillips gave a well-attended public lecture on Cleveland Ironstones in the spectacular new Town Hall, opened in that same year.

As a member of the University, there were also the countless demands on his time in terms of administration and university politics, committees to attend, projects to arrange, consultancy work to be done, papers to write. He continued to work for the BAAS as Assistant Editor of its Annual Reports – 27 in total – until 1862. He retained his cordial links albeit at a distance with the Yorkshire Philosophical Society as one of its active Vice Presidents. He continued to write papers on a huge range of topics for various academic journals. There was constant new research to pursue, including work for what was to become his final major publication the **Geology of Oxford and the Valley of the Thames,** published in 1871 and a revision of his **Illustrations of the Geology of Yorkshire – The Yorkshire Coast** which was not published in 1875.

The death of his sister Anne as a result of a tumour in 1862 was a profound blow to Phillips. Significantly she was buried not in Oxford, but in their adopted city of York, in a simple grave in the city's cemetery,

Leeds Town Hall as it was in the early twentieth century

where twelve years later she was to be joined by her brother. His Christian faith and network of friendships in Oxford supported him at this difficult time. No doubt his endless professional and intellectual activity allowed less time for introspection.

He was still working at the cutting edge of earth sciences, not only in his own research but through the various scientific committees of the BAAS which he was involved with. This included a return to his love of cave archaeology, with new exploration work in Kent's Cavern in Torquay, Devon which he was able to authorise and help finance through BAAS sponsorship (he had been their President in 1865 and still had considerable influence). Perhaps most significant of all to him was a project which brought him in September 1873 for one last time back to the Yorkshire Dales – having attended the BAAS meeting in Bradford a few days before. The purpose of his journey up to Settle with his committee colleagues was to visit Victoria Cave in the high limestone crags of Attermire and Brent Scars, some two miles behind the little market town. Victoria Cave was later described by Kendall and Wroot as *one of the most famous bone-caverns in Britain.*[3]

On the afternoon of September 18th 1873, a wild and rainy day, Phillips and around 20 other suitably attired, middle-aged gentlemen could have been seen following the steep tracks and narrow grassy paths which lead from Settle market place eventually ascending to the entrance of Victoria Cave.[4]

Victoria Cave had been discovered[5] by accident some 36 years previously in 1837 when a young local tinsmith, Michael Horner, out rabbiting with friends, saw his dog disappear into what looked like a large fox hole in the steep hillside then later re-appear out of another hole up the hillside. Puzzled by this, he investigated and soon found himself crawling down a narrow passage into what soon opened out in the blackness of a large cave. He returned to collect a few items of interest found on the floor of the cave, which he later showed to his friend and employer twenty year old local plumber Joseph Jackson. In making a more detailed exploration, Jackson discovered the partly walled up opening leading into the bigger, totally dark, and wet inner chamber. This was beautifully decorated with white stalactites, and stalagmites. Jackson named it Victoria Cave after the young Queen who had recently come to the throne.

Entrance to Victoria Cave as it is now (author)

Over the next few years, Jackson dug inside the cave, especially in the inner chamber, sometimes spending the entire night there working by candlelight. Bit by bit he put together a collection of interesting finds, including beautiful Romano-British crafted bone artefacts and jewellery items. Though he had no archaeological training, Jackson realised the importance of what he was finding. In 1840 he contacted Charles Roach Smith, a leading London archaeologist and expert in Roman history, who was later to become a founder of the British Archaeological Association. Smith also recognised the importance of the discoveries and was soon presenting his "notes" to the Society of Antiquaries.

Jackson continued with his exploration work. But it was the discovery of the jaw of a spotted hyena that caught the attention of that other leading expert on cave palaeontology, William Buckland. Buckland came up to Settle to meet Jackson and see his collection.

By the 1860s such caves with their remarkable preserved animal and human remains were recognised as being a rich source of potential evidence for emerging scientific theories of both animal and human evolution.

In 1869, reflecting this renewed national interest in cave palaeontology and archaeology, Thomas McKenny Hughes, a member of the Geological Survey (who was to succeed Adam Sedgwick as Woodwardian Professor at Cambridge University), set up the Settle Cave Exploration Committee. This was under the chairmanship of Sir James Kay Shuttleworth (1804–77), the noted educationalist and social reformer who was also a Governor of nearby Giggleswick School. The group included several local landowners, academics and enthusiasts such as local landowner and banker Walter Morrison and the Birkbeck family of Settle – a wealthy Quaker family who were millowners and founders and partners of the Craven Bank. Both John Birkbeck senior and his son John Birkbeck junior were keen mountaineers and speleologists. John senior had undertaken pioneering descents of in 1842 of Gaping Gill and in 1845 of Alum Pot, as well as being the conqueror of many Alpine peaks, whilst his equally distinguished son was also a well-known climber and explorer, who became Secretary to the Committee. Other supporters included Professor Adam Sedgwick and James Farrer of Clapham, local landowner amateur archaeologist and early scientist, who had undertaken the major pioneering survey work on Ingleborough Cave on his estate.

Subscriptions were raised by the Committee to fund major new scientific exploration work and excavations of Victoria Cave, and William Boyd Dawkins (1837–1929) was appointed to direct the work. Dawkins, a student of John Phillips, had just left his post with the Geological Survey to become the Curator of the Natural History Department at Owens College, Manchester University, and was soon to be made Professor of Geology at the University. Joseph Jackson, now

William Boyd Dawkins
(British Geological Survey)

MAULL & C$^{\underline{o}}$ LONDON.

in his mid-50s, was paid to be site supervisor in charge of the day to day running of the excavations, and supervising the two workmen employed to dig.

Boyd Dawkins was to publish a detailed description of the first stages of the work undertaken between 1870 and 73 in his seminal book, **Cave Hunting**, in 1874.[6]

The purpose of the visit by the BAAS Committee that wild September day in 1873 was for the special sub-committee to both review what progress had been made on the excavations and to consider what further work should be undertaken. By now the cave was recognised as a nationally important because it contained a bone bed accumulated by spotted hyenas beneath overlain by Glacial sediments.

Phillips' personal interest and enthusiasm would have been important in convincing the BAAS to support the project. He could also ensure involvement of two of his former Oxford students to lead the excavations and scientific research.

This next stage of the work was to be led by another of Phillips' protégés, Boyd Dawkins's former colleague at the Geological Survey, Richard Hill Tiddeman (1842–1917). Tiddeman's work continued until 1878 when it had to be abandoned as funding was exhausted.

This was to be the last visit John Phillips was to make to the Yorkshire Dales. Sadly, the inclement conditions – *"the weather was bad, and dusk came on earlier than was convenient"* – would have denied him a last great view from the Cave entrance across to the nearby Mountain Limestone crags and outcrops down to Attermire Scar and across Warrendale Knotts. From here he should have enjoyed views across the green expanse of Upper Ribblesdale to Smearsett Scar and beyond to the great steps of Yoredale Limestones and cap

Richard Hill Tiddeman, President of Yorkshire Geological Society 1914–5 (British Geological Survey)

The view from the entrance to Victoria Cave across Ribblesdale to the summit of Ingleborough (Dorian Speakman)

of Millstone Grit that form the iconic summit of Ingleborough, all sights which would have been so very familiar to him.

When the party finally reached the cave, they were given talks by Boyd Dawkins and Tiddeman on the "chief bearings and difficulties" facing the archaeologists and palaeontologists who had to work through thick layers of Glacial sediments and collapsed limestone blocks to reach the crucial hyena bone bed

After the visit, the party were invited to look at the new Museum opened at the nearby Giggleswick School; Tiddeman, as Secretary of the BAAS Committee, recorded *"Professor Phillips in particular being very warm in his admiration"*. The party were then *"most hospitably entertained"* by the Birkbecks.

A remarkable photograph exists of the Victoria Cave party, with by that time white side-whiskered Phillips among the group. This was almost certainly the last image of the Professor ever captured. He seems to have combined his attendance at the BAAS Annual Meeting at Bradford and the Settle expedition with what was also to be his last social visit to York, to revisit the Museum and meet some of his many York friends.[7]

In later years, John Phillips would have been saddened to learn of the bitter dispute that developed between his two former students, Boyd Dawkins and Tiddeman. Tiddeman demonstrated that the bone bed accumulated by hyenas at Victoria Cave with its remains of hippopotamus and extinct forms of elephant and rhinoceros had formed during to a warm period *within* the Ice Age. He then went on to show that the sequence of Ice Age sediments at Victoria Cave revealed that this warm event was both proceeded and followed by periods of Glaciation. Tiddeman's work at Victoria Cave provided the first ever geological evidence for cyclical climate change during the Ice Age.[8] However, these findings directly challenged Dawkins' ideas about the Ice Age. Anxious to protect his own scientific reputation Dawkins vigorously set about dismissing Tiddeman's claims.[9]

A few weeks after the BAAS visit, on the 7th October, the Committee received a communication from Professor George Busk (1807–1886) an expert on Ice Age animal bones, an authority on the identification of ancient human remains and a friend of Darwin. Busk told the Committee he had just identified a bone from the hyena bone bed as part of a human fibula, the smaller of the two lower leg bones, and being found beneath glacial sediments, it represented the oldest evidence so far recognised for ancient humans in Europe. Busk encouraged the Committee to continue with the excavations, now awarded an annual grant of £100 by the BAAS. Busk was especially keen for the excavations to find an ancient human skull in the hyena bone bed.[10] This was all part of the contemporary interest in Darwin's still highly contentious theory of evolution, and the search for a "missing link", a term made popular by Thomas Huxley in the 1860s to describe as at that time undiscovered skeletal evidence to connect modern humans to an ape like ancestor.

Tiddeman, despite his meticulous efforts over the next four years, never found further human remains to support his theory, and the damage to his reputation was a contributory factor for funding for further work at Victoria Cave not being renewed after 1878.

Tiddeman continued to do brilliant work for the Geological Survey, including seminal work on the classic limestone areas of Dales, and important work on the great Craven Reef Knolls[11] and explaining the faulting and uplift of what is known as the Askrigg Dome in the northern

The Settle Exploration Committee and BAAS Sub Committee members, September 1873. John Phillips is sitting in the bottom row right (© Tom Lord Collection)

Yorkshire Dales, work for which he received the Murchison Medal in 1911. Though he became President of the Yorkshire Geological Society in 1914, he never received full recognition for his major work on the Quaternary Deposits at Victoria Cave during his own lifetime.[12]

Thirty years later, further research elsewhere proved that Tiddeman was absolutely right. This has also been confirmed by more recent research including radiometric dating of stalagmites found in Victoria Cave. Over the last 600,000 years there have been four periods of glaciation and six warmer interglacial periods. As the Settle archaeologist and historian Tom Lord has shown,[13] in many ways Tiddeman was the better, the more meticulous researcher, whilst Boyd Dawkins allowed his preconceptions to stand in the way of pragmatic evidence.

Other material found by Jackson, Dawkins, Tiddeman and others in subsequent excavations from the Cave have provided a rich picture of

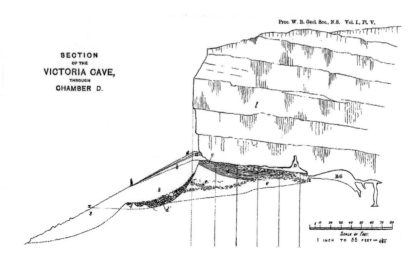

Proc. W. R. Geol. Soc., N.S.   Vol. I., Pl. V.

SECTION
OF THE
VICTORIA CAVE,
THROUGH
CHAMBER D.

Drawing of inside of Victoria Cave – taken from Tiddeman's paper in the **Proceedings of the GPSWRY 1875** Vol 6.

changing climatic conditions and of human and animal occupation of the area. Major recent finds by have included a decorated reindeer antler rod, carbon dated to between 12,521 and 12,434 BC – at present time the oldest dated human artefact found in Yorkshire, butchered wild horse bones from a similar period and the celebrated Upper Palaeolithic bone harpoon dating back to 10,853–10,846 BC. These finds prove that early man was using the cave for shelter and as a retreat, as human occupation and activity gradually returned to what is now the North of England at the end of the last Ice Age.[14]

Hyena Crania discovered in Victoria Cave 1872–3. These would have been seen by John Phillips in Giggleswick School Museum in September 1873 (© Tom Lord Collection)

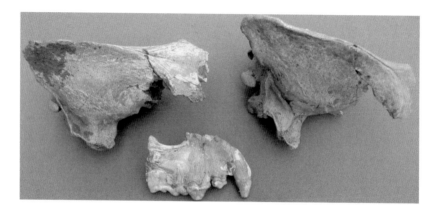

Professor Phillips – photographer unknown probably taken in the early 1870s
(British Geological Survey)

What excited John Phillips about Victoria Cave was his realisation that it offered the potential to be what we would now describe as a "time capsule". The 1870–78 project, and later excavations, have unearthed evidence from over 600,000 years of the earth's history, well beyond the imagined years of Genesis. Finds which have been recorded include the remains of Palaeolithic fauna – hyena, ancient elephants, rhinoceros and cave bear, bears having not dissimilar requirements for shelter to early humans, and also many early implements and tools as well as later Roman-British artefacts and jewellery.

The visit to Victoria Cave in 1873 was therefore important to John Phillips because it brought together and confirmed so much of his life's work as a geologist and palaeontologist. Indeed the experience must have echoed the visit to a cave he had made almost half a century previously, at Kirkdale, when he had first come to Yorkshire as his uncle's young assistant.

So for a short period in that epoch of constantly challenging and changing technology and ideas, the research carried out by John Phillips' students at Victoria Cave was at the cutting edge of our understanding of mankind's place in the long story of the evolution of the earth.

It was therefore fitting, that on his last visit to the Yorkshire Dales, John Phillips, a man who had done so much to unravel the complex rock structures of the great coastal and limestone landscapes of Yorkshire, should see this next generation of scientists developing new techniques and new lines of enquiry into the frontiers of knowledge of the origins of humankind; research that was to continue in the hands of generations to come.

John Phillips unexpectedly died just seven months after this Settle visit. On the evening of April 23rd, 1874, after dinner with friends at All Souls College, Oxford, when chatting to three senior colleagues as they walked down a narrow connecting corridor where coffee was to be served, Phillips stumbled on a mat. He fell over backwards down a flight of 15 stone steps. He received critical injuries that left him paralysed. He never recovered consciousness and died the following day.

Notes

1. Davis James 1889 *Biographical Notes of Eminent Yorkshire Geologists No IV Hugh Edwin Strickland* in Proceedings of the GPSWRY Proceedings 11 (2) pp139–154

2. Quoted in Hunter Robert in Phillips Obituary The Athenaeum 2427 May 1874 pp597–8

3. Kendall PF and Wroot HE 1924 *The Geology of Yorkshire* Leeds: authors p947

4. Tiddeman RH 1875 *Second report of the Committee appointed for the purpose of assisting in the Exploration of the Settle Caves* (Victoria Cave): BAAS 44th Meeting Annual Report p133

5. Lord Tom 2005 *The Discovery of Victoria Cave* in North Craven Heritage Trust Journal 2005 p5

6. Boyd Dawkins William 1874 *Cave Hunting* London: Macmillan pp35–39

7. York Herald Friday 1 May 1874

8. Tiddeman RH 1875 *The Work and Problems of the Victoria Cave Exploration*: GPSWRY Proceedings 1875 Vol 6 pp77–92

9. White Mark John 2017 *William Dawkins and the Victorian Science of Cave Hunting – Three Men in a Cavern* Barnsley: Pen & Sword pp91–97

10. Kendall PF & Wroot HE 1924 *op. cit.* pp580–585

11. Tiddeman R.H. 1890 *Physical History of the Carboniferous Rocks in Upper Airedale* GPSWRY Proceedings Vol 11 pp482–92

12. Cooper Anthony H. 2016 *Yorkshire Geology as seen through the eyes of notable British Geological Survey geologists 1862–2000* in Myerscough, R and Wallace, V. Famous Geologists of Yorkshire York: Place pp51–55

13. Lord Tom 2013: *Victoria Cave Revisited*: Settle: Museum of Northern Craven Life,

14. Howard J and Lord T 2013 *Cave Archaeology – in Caves and Karst of the Yorkshire Dales* Buxton: British Cave Research Association p239–51

Mill Gill Force, Askrigg, Wensleydale (Dorian Speakman)

8

The Legacy

The sudden death of John Phillips on April 23rd 1874, literally in mid conversation and still at the height of his creative and intellectual powers, shocked everyone in the academic world, but in his adopted city of York, this groundswell went well beyond just the great and the good. The people of York were welcoming back in death one of their own.

His funeral was extended across the two cities. On Wednesday 29th April in Oxford a procession of 150 people, including many from the University in academic dress, followed his coffin as it was taken from his home, at Museum House, across the city to the railway station, to be transported to York, *"this ancient city with whom he identified himself and which he loved as his own home*[1]*"*, where it was carried from the train to be laid overnight in the vestibule at the York Museum.

The morning of 30th April was a beautiful day and as the York Herald reported:[2]

> *Only a limited number were admitted to the hall of the
> Museum, where the coffin was placed, on which lay a splendid
> garland of immortelles (everlasting flowers). The funeral
> drapery, and the novel purpose to which the spacious vestibule
> was devoted, imparted a most impressive solemnity of the scene,
> which could not be beheld by those ardently attached to the late
> Professor without calling forth indications of poignant grief at
> the loss of whom they all revered ...*[3]

With the Great Bell of York Minister solemnly tolling for a full 90 minutes, joined by the smaller bell of St Olave's church where both Phillips and his sister Anne had been regular worshippers, no other sound breaking the silence apart from bird song, the cortege wound its way through the Museum Gardens to the little church on Marygate. Here the Venerable Archdeacon William Hey, an old friend of Phillips, read part of the Service of the Dead. After this short service, no less than thirty carriages were waiting in Marygate to follow the coffin across the city to the Cemetery, over a mile away. It is recorded that almost every shop and business in the city was closed and house curtains drawn out of respect, and the whole route was lined with spectators. In attendance were many of his former colleagues from Oxford, as well as from other parts of England, York City Councillors, plus representatives from the Yorkshire Philosophical Society, and the Geological and Polytechnic Society of the West Riding of Yorkshire. There were also many other officers and members from the many naturalist and scientific groups from all over Yorkshire that Phillips had supported over many decades.

John Phillips was laid to rest in the grave under a simple stone slab alongside his beloved sister Anne, with the final part of the Burial Service read to the large group of attendant mourners by Archdeacon Hey who had presided over Anne's burial 12 years previously.

On the following Sunday, in York Minster, William Hey gave a moving tribute to Phillips in his sermon, which as well as referring to the professor's ability to reconcile science and Christian belief, paid tribute to a remarkable personality:

> For years he lived among us as the central moving spirit of all scientific inquiry; as the smoother of all acrimony; the reconciler of all differences ...

> A great man, an eminent man; a man who devoted his high scientific attainments to practical and useful things, has been taken from us, but it is not only on account of his high intellectual acquirements that I desire to speak words of loving memory here. I would rather speak of one whose honours never seemed for one moment to diminish the simplicity and the humility of his character. You might see him surrounded by those noble in rank, and by the highest in learning – himself recognised as one of the foremost among them, but you never saw any deviation from that quiet simplicity and from straightforward speech and thought. I would rather speak of one who from first and last showed the same warm, living and kind heart, he was never so happy as when he was helping others; never so happy as when he was forwarding the interests and guiding the minds of young men.

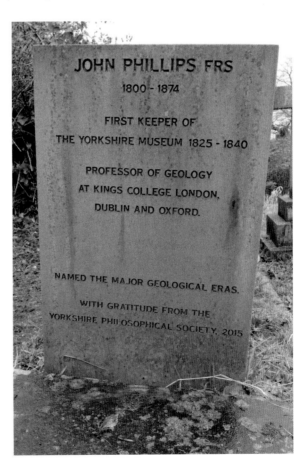

Headstone erected in 2015 by the YPS to mark John Phillips' grave in York Cemetery

The many societies and associations that Phillips had links with over the previous half century filled their pages with words of appreciation. For example, the Yorkshire Philosophical Society in their Annual Report for 1875, as well as listing Phillips' many achievements, including over 70 learned academic papers and books, extensively quoted William Thomson, the Archbishop of York, a President of the Society:

> *I have known many scientific men, but none who seems to me*
> *to have more of the metal and temper of the philosopher than*
> *Professor Phillips. The patience in research, the acuteness of*
> *observation, the eye and hand of an artist for natural scenery,*
> *the cheerfulness of temper which naturalists seem often to attain*
> *in the peaceful field of their labour, the unaffected piety, the*
> *reasonable caution which is so needful of a counterpoise to the*
> *pride and overconfidence of successful research; all these seemed*
> *to me to meet in him, one of the most agreeable, as he was one*
> *of the clearest instructors in the secrets of the great Book of*
> *God's creation.*[4]

Dr John Evans, the then President of the Geological Society of London, in his memorial address for Phillips in 1875, captures an essential quality of just how skilfully John Phillips could operate to secure compromise and get others to support his ways of thinking:

> *Eminently judicious, ever courteous, genial, and conciliatory,*
> *he gained the affection of all with whom he was brought into*
> *contact; whilst in cases where conflicting view required to be*
> *reduced into harmony and strong feelings to be smoothed,*
> *his tact and judgements were often to prevail where the more*
> *strenuous efforts of others would have been powerless.*[5]

James Davis, at that time Honorary Secretary of the GPSWRY, who had met Phillips at the 1873 British Association meeting in Bradford, gives in his 1882 **Biographical Notices of Eminent Yorkshire Geologists**, a first-hand account of Phillips' likeable personality:

> *my recollection is very fresh of his kind and genial face, his*
> *winning and encouraging smile, the ever-ready and wise*
> *words which he brightened and enlivened the most perplexing*

question and the deep knowledge which lay below and
prompted all his observations.[6]

Davis also goes on to stress Phillips' huge contribution to the teaching
of students, through his lecturing and pastoral encouragement work. He
was *an inculcator of true knowledge and scientific methods in youthful minds.*

The Hull geologist Thomas Sheppard, in his YGS Presidential address of
1932 on the subject of John Phillips provides a valuable summary of Phillips'
many achievements, (including further details of his work in Bielsbeck in the
Yorkshire Wolds and his lectures in Hull) also touches on another aspect of
the remarkable intellectual energy and creativity of his subject:

> *When the number of books which Phillips not only wrote but*
> *illustrated is realised, and the enormous quantity of good*
> *scientific knowledge put in a readable manner, it is amazing to*
> *think that he was able to accomplish anything other than write*
> *in the whole of his lifetime.*[7]

His textbooks on geology including the 1834 **Guide to Geology, A
Treatise on Geology** of 1837 and the **Manual of Geology** of 1855, were
much reprinted and were standard works of reference for students of
geology for some decades.

"Genius" is an overused word. In Phillips' case it might be safer to refer
to his penetrating intellect, capable of absorbing facts, information and
concepts at extraordinary speed, classifying and analysing often complex
palaeontological information with brilliance, and making connections
between different ideas and concepts with impressive speed. Three other
factors that made him remarkable were his creative energy, enthusiasm
and limitless curiosity.

What is beyond dispute is Phillips' complete mastery of so many
different related scientific disciplines, including not only geology and
palaeontology, but archaeology, botany, zoology, meteorology, and
astronomy. This allowed him to bring cross-disciplinary insights as well
as practical skills into every aspect of his teaching and research. Yet with
perhaps a degree of self-conscious false modesty he described himself as
merely a "contemplative naturalist.[8]"

In his Yorkshire years, Phillips had an unrivalled range of experience in many key roles of research, teaching and administration, skills that were to come to fruition in Oxford in his University career. He also had a major role in developing, in Oxford, one of the finest Natural History Museums in the British Isles, if not Europe.

As Jack Morrell comments:

> Over a period of thirty years he was a provincial museum keeper, a public lecturer, an encyclopaedist, an employee of the Geological Survey, Professor of King's College London and Trinity College Dublin, a government commissioner, an occasional consultant, the key administrator of the British Association, the writer of popular books about Yorkshire, a reviewer for the weekly the Athenaeum.[9]

To this list might be added his skill as a draughtsman, cartographer[10] and even artist. This is revealed not only for the drawings of fossils that illustrate many of his books, works of art in themselves, but his deft landscapes in his topographical books, sea cliffs, crags, waterfalls. These were of a quality that most professional artists would be proud to be able to deliver.

With his practical skills – going back to his days on the road with William Smith – he was also a clever technician, inventing improved barometers and other measuring instruments. For the 1851 Great Exhibition he entered five inventions for display in the Inventions section: an electrophorus (used in electrical experiments), a rain gauge, a maximum thermometer, a cardboard anemometer, and an air barometer for use in mines. Two of these inventions were given an honourable mention by judges.[11]

In so many ways, John Phillips was the prototype for a recognisably modern, meritocratic figure, the professional academic scientist. Like many others who were to follow him, he came from a humble background, yet succeeded partly through his immense natural ability, but also through endless hard work, ambition and application helped by general good health, and for most periods of his life, a remarkably balanced temperament.

As Morrell points out, for Phillips life was always about "making ends meet". Until his appointment at Oxford, which finally gave him financial security, every decision and life choice he made – no doubt remembering his uncle's frequent periods of financial plight – was about ensuring there was a safety net of a regular income, however modest, coming in to his household, both for himself, and for much of his life, for his sister. Science was a passion – but the scientist also has to eat and have a roof over his head. That meant securing a regular salary – not as William Smith had to endure, the fluctuating patronage of wealthy landowners and industrialists.

One of the great achievements of the British Association, an achievement in which Phillips also had a key role, was to raise the social standing and renumeration of scientists as a valued profession – though this took years to achieve.

What is the relevance of John Phillips and his many achievements for the twenty-first century?

John Phillips' Memorial window in St. Olave's Church

Unlike the artist, musician or poet, the work of a scientist does not have a permanent existence outside space and time. Science always moves onward. The work of one generation of scientists builds on the work of the last. But in so doing new work partly obliterates the old. What was a cutting edge theory for one generation is often proved less than adequate by later workers in the field.

But in the inspiring words used by Sir Isaac Newton *If I have seen a little further, it is by standing on the shoulders of Giants.*[12]

John Phillips was one of those Giants on whose shoulders later generations of nineteenth and twentieth century scientists could indeed stand. His contribution to science was about far more than individual facts of strata or fossils. It was more about exemplifying the fundamental essential integrity and honesty of the empirical scientist, who must look at recorded facts and take whatever journeys of enquiry those facts may direct them, even, as in Phillips' case, if those quests for truth raise uncomfortable issues that may collide with long held beliefs and personal faith.

Given the huge challenges of the twenty-first century, the integrity, honesty and courage of men and women of science of the calibre of John Phillips are needed like never before.

In 1961 the Yorkshire Geological Society launched a biennial award in the name of their illustrious Second Honorary Member (William Smith being the First), known as the Phillips Medal:

> which shall be awarded not more frequently than biennially,
> shall be an acknowledgement of distinguished contributions
> to, or of work bearing upon, knowledge of the stratigraphy or
> palaeontology of the north of England.[13]

The Phillips Medal continues to be awarded on a regular basis for outstanding achievements in these twin fields.

The other enduring aspect of Phillips' work was his gift as a communicator. He could enthuse and inspire an audience through his skill with the spoken words like few other scientists in history. At the last of the series of four lectures given in 1853 to the Leeds Mechanics

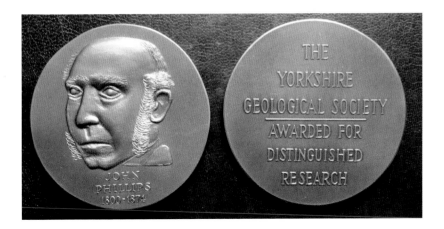

The John Phillips Medal (YGS)

and Literary Institute, the reaction of the audience of mixed social backgrounds for this sober series of lectures,(though no doubt enlivened by a reference to the bones of hippos being discovered in a brick field near Wellington Bridge in central Leeds) is recorded by the Leeds Intelligencer:

> The cheering on the conclusion of the lecture was hearty and prolonged. We may add that we think such a course of lectures admirably adapted to give Yorkshiremen a correct idea of the wonderful works of the creator – their beauty and harmony – and to impart an additional zest to their walks and excursions, and a more enlightened perception of natural objects whether flourishing above or entombed beneath the surface.[14]

There is little doubt, that had Phillips lived in the age of mass media and television, he would have soon become a household name.

His terminology – Palaeozoic, Mesozoic and Cainozoic – to describe the ancient eras, based on fossil evidence of the earth's earliest recognisable plant and animal species, is still used in scientific literature worldwide, so in that sense alone Phillips made a contribution to world science. He was among the first to popularise the concept of "Deep Time" in terms of the age of the earth in relation the relatively short history – in geological terms – of the human species, though time-frames have grown massively in scale since Phillips' day.

Science writer Peter Brannen credits Phillips as one of the first scientific figures to fully recognise, as early as 1860, the significance – from palaeontological evidence – of what we now know to have been the five great "Mass Extinctions" of animal, fish and plant life that almost wiped out life on the planet since Ordovician times. Brennan suggests that Phillips believed only divine intervention, in the form of new creations of species, saved life on earth after the End-Permian Mass Extinction of 252 million years ago.[15]

Martin Rudwick shows how it was only in the 1980s, and after exhaustive statistical analysis of the fossil records, that research by Raup and Sepkoski proved that Phillips' classification system was essentially correct, if way ahead of its time:

> the two events with the greatest apparent rates of extinction were at the boundaries between the Permian period and the Triassic and between the Cretaceous and the Tertiary. This confirmed, with a hugely enlarged body of evidence, what Phillips had judged over a century earlier, when he used these points to define the boundaries between the three great eras in the history of life, the Palaeozoic, Mesozoic and Cenozoic.[16]

One wonders what Phillips' reactions would have been, to the recent Intergovernmental Science Policy Statement[17] on the horrifying human-caused loss, worldwide, of the world's rich heritage of animal, insect and plant species and of biodiversity. Many scientists are now suggesting that this might, unless reversed by immediate international co-operation and action, be the start of a Sixth Mass Extinction – and one which, if it occurs, could take mankind with it.

In terms of his achievements as a topographical writer, John Phillips had a crucial role in interpreting the great landscapes of Yorkshire. His were the first accurate analyses of the geology of Yorkshire's dramatic Coast, Dales and Moors, and his descriptions have had an influence on all later generations of serious topographical writers, whether or not they were aware of the name of John Phillips when they first walked or drove through these same landscapes. Whenever the name "Yoredale" is used for the high limestone crags of Wensleydale or Swaledale, or "Tabular Hills" on the North York Moors, we are paying unconscious tribute

The entrance to Ingleborough Cave, Clapdale near Clapham. In **The Rivers, Mountains and Sea Coast of Yorkshire** Phillips gives a detailed description of the physical and chemical processes that, over millennia, created this remarkable cave system (Ingleborough Cave Ltd)

to one of the great walker-interpreters of the Yorkshire Dales and the North York Moors, a man who had a detailed, personal knowledge of the remotest part of the Dales, Moors and North Pennines that few have ever equalled. But he also brought a rare passion and sense of the uniqueness of place to this knowledge and understanding, demonstrated both by his two volumes of the **Illustrations of the Geology of Yorkshire** and by his two popular guidebooks **Rivers, Mountain and Sea Coast of Yorkshire**, and **Excursions from the North Eastern Railway.** These are all still very readable accounts of much of what makes Yorkshire such a unique and special region.

A common theme of much of Phillips' work is that of the constant interaction of space and time – how particular places have been shaped and given a special identity by the action of natural processes over aeons, as indicated by the geological and palaeontological evidence. Often a telling detail – usually in Phillips' case a geological observation – can make a description of a place come alive. But he was also interested in the more recent human impact – the local archaeology and history, and all that gives a particular location its unique sense of place. This is what makes his travel writing so rewarding.

This enthusiasm and insight were constantly shared with others, initially through his lectures but over a longer period through his writing. This was then passed both directly and indirectly to later generations of professional and amateur scientific explorers – geologists, palaeontologists, botanists, biologists, archaeologists. Teachers at every level, from university departments to primary school classes, have shared in this role of dissemination. Even visitors with more superficial interests in areas like the Dales and Moors who nonetheless have a love for the area have often been influenced and guided by Phillips' later disciples. This leads into a greater understanding of what they see in the landscape they were looking at or places they were visiting, and what makes them distinctive and special. In those many wild and beautiful places which he has described, John Phillips has been a constant, if mostly unseen, presence.

That influence has been spread through interlocking networks of voluntary societies including many of those that Phillips helped to set up or encouraged such as the Yorkshire Philosophical Society, the Yorkshire Geological Society, or those which emerged in later years such as the Yorkshire Archaeological Society, Yorkshire Naturalists Union and Yorkshire Wildlife Trust as well as the many local naturalists', geological and archaeological societies. This influence, in countless ways, remains undiminished.

Phillips' insights into what makes Yorkshires landscapes distinctive and special have been repeated and shared not only with those with access to his own well-read articles and books, but also by later generations of writers who added their own research and insights to this shared knowledge. In our region this included men and women such as Harry Speight, Percy Kendal, Herbert Wroot, Frank Elgee, Harry Speight, Alfred J. Brown, Arthur Raistrick, Ella Pontefract, Marie Hartley, Joan Ingilby, Alfred Wainwright, Richard Muir, and many, many more besides, all sharing Phillips' passion for getting out into the countryside on their own two feet, walking the moorland, mountain, riverside and cliff top paths, with rucksack and Ordnance Map, hammer, magnifying glass, collecting box or camera, or maybe just their own memory, looking at and eventually recording in print or picture their knowledge of and insight into the natural world and the historic, cultural landscape. Often they took exactly the same rural train journeys from the cities to the countryside used by Phillips and his contemporaries or after road transport competition and Beeching had closed many of the rural rail branches, by the country bus and private car.

By the mid-twentieth century they, and their many thousands of followers, became active members of walking, cycling and outdoor clubs such as The Ramblers, Holiday Fellowship, CHA, The Clarion, Camping Club, the YHA. There was also the wider countryside preservation movement including bodies such as The National Trust, The Council for the Protection of Rural England, The Campaign for National Parks, National Park Societies, and a whole range of local wildlife and naturalists' groups. Combining their efforts, they created the strong, unstoppable political pressures to legally safeguard these special areas as a precious educational and health-giving resource for Britain's largely urban population. This was achieved through the great post-War 1949 National Parks and Access to the Countryside Act, a piece of visionary legislation, of which John Phillips, the democrat and lecturer to Mechanics Institutes, would have thoroughly approved. Equally we can imagine he would have supported subsequent legislation such as the Countryside and Rights of Way (CROW) Act of 2000 that

opened up so much of the open moorland of our National Parks and Pennine Moorlands as well as the dry valleys of the Wolds for legal access on foot for geologists, archaeologists and naturalists. Or equally he would have enjoyed the simple carefree, natural freedom and beauty to be experienced by any casual walker exploring the limestone scars and crags of Ingleborough or Whernside, meandering riversides paths along Esk or Swale, or the wide grass-covered summits of the Howgill Fells.

A lone walker in the Howgill Fells
(Dorian Speakman)

Yorkshire now has a magnificent legacy of National Parks covering the North York Moors and the Yorkshire Dales, three Areas of Outstanding Natural Beauty, in Nidderdale, the Howardian Hills and the Forest of Bowland, as well as the dramatic Yorkshire Heritage Coast, and several National Nature Reserves. Much of this protected landscape, if sadly somewhat under-resourced, is also accessible by several long-distance National Trails – The Pennine Way, The Cleveland Way, The Yorkshire Wolds Way and The Pennine Bridleway – Trails authorised by the same Act of Parliament of 1949 – as well as many other more recently devised walking and cycling routes. What they have in common is that they all pass through areas accurately described and celebrated almost two centuries ago by John Phillips, scientist, artist, passionate walker and lover of Yorkshire.

These places and these trails are his enduring memorials.

Sunrise from Cleveland Way, north of Scalby Ness (Tom Mutton, NYMNPA)

Notes

1   York Herald 4 May 1874
2   York Herald 1 May 1874
3   *Ibid.* 1874
4   York Herald 4 May 1874
5   Davis James 1889 *History of the Yorkshire Geological and Polytechnic Society, 1837–1887. With biographical notices of some of its members* Leeds: GPSWRY p119–136
6   Davis James 1882 Proceedings of the Yorkshire Geological and Polytechnic Society Vi VIII pp3–20
7   Sheppard T. 1933 Proceedings of the GPSWRY 1932 pp153–187
8   Phillips John *1860 Life on Earth: Its Origin and Succession* London: Longmans – Preface p1
9   Morrell Jack 2005 *op. cit.* p518
10 Douglas JA & Edmonds JM 1950 *John Phillips 's Geological Maps of the British Isles* in Annals of Science, Vol 6, No 4 November 1950
11 *Ibid.* p323–4
12 Newton Isaac 1676 Letter to Robert Hooke
13 Yorkshire Geological Society Proceedings Vol 33 Annual Report 1961 p1
14 Leeds Intelligencer April 30th 1853
15 Brannen Peter 2017 *The Ends of the Earth.* London: One World p110
16 Rudwick, Martin *Earth's Deep History.* Chicago & London Chicago University Press p269,
17 *Summary for policymakers of the global assessment report on biodiversity and eco system services of the Intergovernmental Science Policy Platform on Biodiversity and Ecosystem services* 2019 pp1–39

Walkers on the Cleveland Way above Staithes (NYMNPA)

9

In the footsteps of John Phillips

Despite the passage of almost two centuries, the majority of natural and even man-made features that John Phillips described in his **Illustrations of the Geology of Yorkshire**, **Rivers, Mountains and Sea-Coast of Yorkshire** or **Excursions from the North Eastern Railway** as well as in his very many articles and academic papers, can be seen much as Phillips described them, even if many branch railways have disappeared, new roads built or buildings have been demolished or rebuilt.

What has evolved is the science of geology. Through a process of constant refinement and sub-classification, terminology has changed. Phillips' broad-brush treatment of strata, faults and structures have been re-examined, corrected and constantly improved. Huge advances in techniques and conceptual frameworks, with endless subdivisions and redefinitions of detail, have now moved the science onwards, away from those vitally important foundations laid down by Smith, Phillips and so many other workers.

Even modern field guides must be constantly revised to absorb new discoveries as technology advances and new recording methods develop.

To understand more about the landscape that Phillips was first describing, there are several excellent, well-illustrated modern published guides to Yorkshire's geology which without undermining Phillips' work can help put it in perspective.

In terms of the Yorkshire Coast, North York Moors and Yorkshire Wolds, perhaps the best available guide is the **Geology of the Yorkshire Coast** (4th edition 2018) by Peter Rawson and John Wright, together with other contributors, published by the Geologists' Association (Guide no 34). As well as giving a superb overview to the geology of the area, there are seventeen "Itineraries" – walks or sometimes drives to specific locations in the area where strata, faulting or other phenomena can be easily be seen. The book comes with suitable warnings about access and safety in a cliff and coastal environment.

For the novice geologist, however, an excellent starting point is Roger Osborne's illustrated booklet **The Dinosaur Coast – Yorkshire Rocks, Fossils and Landscape** published by Hightide Publishing (2015) in partnership with Scarborough Museums Trust and the North York Moors National Park. **Rocks & Landscapes of the North York Moors** (2018) in the same series gives an excellent overview of the whole of the North York Moors, including the Tabular Hills in the south of the National Park first surveyed by Phillips in 1826–7.

Tony Waltham's classic **Yorkshire Dales Landscape and Geology** (Crowood Press 2007) offers a detailed and highly readable overview of the great Carboniferous Limestone, Millstone Grit and cave areas of the Yorkshire Dales, as first recorded in detail by Phillips. Essential reading too is the Yorkshire Geological Society's Field Guide, **Yorkshire Rocks and Landscape** edited by Colin Scrutton (YGS 1994), which covers the whole of Yorkshire, with a series of authoritative essays by leading experts from the Society, together with detailed itineraries and maps of how to get to specific locations including several within the Yorkshire Dales described by Phillips. Especially useful is a detailed Glossary of common technical terms used by geologists and palaeontologists.

As suggested in chapters 2, 3 and 4, admirers of both William Smith and John Phillips will find much of interest in the **Yorkshire Museum** in York and the **Rotunda Museum** in Scarborough.

Not only do the geological and archaeological collections of the **Yorkshire Museum** still contain material collected from the era when John Phillips was the Museum Keeper, but there is also opportunity to admire a rare copy of the great Smith 1815 Map, the portraits of both Smith and

Phillips and much more besides. The Museum Gardens including the little Observatory building are much as Phillips, Vernon Harcourt and Henry Baines knew them. There is a blue plaque on the wall of St Mary's Lodge as a memorial of its most celebrated tenant, and in St Olave's Church nearby you will see a somewhat neglected memorial window to John Phillips, and close by the former bowling green pavilion beyond the Abbey ruins, you will find the Yorkshire Section of the 1815 Smith Map in coloured pebbles.

The elegant **Rotunda – William Smith Museum of Geology**, just off Scarborough main's sea front, is a place of pilgrimage for anyone with an interest not just in geology, but of that remarkable pre-Victorian period in Yorkshire and English science. The central circular staircase and display area are much as Smith and Phillips and the pioneers of the Scarborough Philosophical Society knew them, and Phillips' famous coloured section of the Yorkshire Coast is superbly displayed. The William Smith Trail through some of the historic buildings and areas of central Scarborough, rich in associations of both Smith and Phillips provides an introduction to their time in Scarborough. The Rotunda Geology Group (www.rotundageologygroup.org) organise a programme of regular events in Scarborough and field visits along the coast so well known to Smith and Phillips, as well as excursions inland.

Further along the coast, the fascinating **Whitby Museum** in Pannett Park founded in 1823 and still owned and managed by the Whitby Literary and Philosophical Society (www.whitbymuseum.org.uk) the Museum has a nationally important collection of Jurassic fossils including several magnificent sea-reptiles such as teleosaurs (marine crocodiles), plesiosaurus and ichthyosaurs and a great collection of ammonites, including several holotypes – the type example of which the first description of the species is based – recorded by local geologists. There is also a fine collection of finds from the Kirkdale Cave, and material relating to the pioneering work of Reverend George Young, John Bird, and John Phillips himself including actual fossils samples used to illustrated their work. There is also material referring to the gifted young geologists Lewis Hunton (1814–1838) from nearby Loftus. Hunton died tragically young of tuberculosis but his brilliant 1836 paper on the relationship of sub-species of ammonites in particular strata in Boulby

Cliff, building on the work of Smith and Phillips, is regarded as one of the cornerstones of the modern science of biostratigraphy. Hunton has an ammonite named after him – *Tragophylloceras huntoni*. This was discovered in 1843 by the energetic Martin Simpson, (1800–1892), Whitby Museum's first curator and a remarkable fossil hunter in his own right.

Pannett Park has an attractive Jurassic Trail within the gardens along which coloured bands record each era of time. Fossils of the Lower, Middle and Upper Jurassic are modelled into the path. Alongside, at appropriate points, are planted modern relatives of the typical ferns and trees that flourished in Jurassic times such as gingkoes and *Araucaria araucana* – the celebrated Victorian monkey puzzle tree – which when fossilised under pressure transforms to the popular Whitby jet, which is also displayed in the Museum in the form of many elaborately carved, mainly Victorian artefacts.

Displays and exhibitions in the two North York Moors National Park Centres at **Sutton Bank** and **Danby Lodge**, whilst frequently changing, often explore themes such as the iron, alum and jet production activity which have shaped the landscape and culture of the National Park.

In terms of the geology and archaeology of the Yorkshire Wolds area, including the coast and Humber foreshore, the **Hull and East Riding Museum** in the Museum Quarter of Hull has a collection of natural objects and artefacts that cover two hundred million years of Wolds and East Riding geology, archaeology and history.

Geology and prehistoric culture of the Yorkshire Dales form much of the collection of artefacts in the **Craven Museum** in Skipton, including the geological and fossil collections of local geologists and historians, including material from Victoria Cave and relics from the lead mines and textile mills of the Yorkshire Dales. The little **Museum of North Craven Life** in The Folly in Settle has displays relating to local geology and prehistory of this part of the Yorkshire Dales including some Victoria Cave material and items from the Tot Lord archaeological collection. Lead mining and quarrying also form a central focus of the **Nidderdale Museum** in the old workhouse, in King Street in Pateley Bridge.

The three excellent Show Caves in the Yorkshire Dales also give insight into early geological exploration and discovery by Phillips and his contemporaries. These are at White Scar Cave at Ingleton, Ingleborough Cave at Clapham, (as actually described by Phillips in **Rivers, Mountains and Sea Coast of Yorkshire**) and Stump Cross, Greenhow, which Phillips was among the first to explore in the 1820s with local lead miners.

It is interesting to reflect that when William Smith and John Phillips first visited the Yorkshire Dales, including their visit to the Old Gang Mines near Gunnerside in Swaledale, the lead mines were in full production. The intimate **Swaledale Museum** in Reeth contains much written, photographic and other material relating to the lead mining and other industries of Swaledale, as does the **Richmondshire Museum** in Ryders Wynd, Richmond.

The Dales Countryside Museum, situated in the old station buildings in Hawes run by the Yorkshire Dales National Park has, as well as local geological displays, a replicated lead mine, and the nationally important Hartley-Ingilby collection of Dales farming and industrial artefacts, recently augmented by important geological and lead mining collections from the now closed Earby Mining Museum.

Finally, there is no better way of understanding the geology of an area, as both Smith and Phillips understood it, then by getting your feet dirty looking and experiencing the rock beneath those feet. **The Yorkshire Geological Society** (yorksgeolsoc.org.uk) in addition to its many publications and regular scholarly Proceedings, organises events and regular field trips throughout the historic county of Yorkshire where with expert guidance, complex geological phenomena are unravelled. Likewise the **Yorkshire Philosophical Society** (www.ypsyork.org) offer regular lectures and talks dealing with many different aspects of the natural and scientific history of Yorkshire. Each year the Society makes an award, appropriately enough known as the **"John & Anne Phillips Prize"** for the best final year undergraduate geology mapping dissertation at the University of Hull.

Select Bibliography

1. Principal Books by John Phillips

(*Most of these books are available via Arkose Press/Book Depository/Amazon in digital format or as facsimile reprint on demand*)

Illustrations of the Geology of Yorkshire or a description of the strata and organic remains of the Yorkshire Coast – 1829 York: Author

A Guide to Geology 1834 London: Longmans

Illustrations of the Geology of Yorkshire or a description of the strata and organic remains: Part II the Mountain Limestone District – 1836 London: John Murray

A Treatise on Geology 1837/9 London: Longmans

Memoirs of William Smith LL.D 1844 London: John Murray (Reprinted 1978 London: Arno Press)

A Manual of Geology 1855 London & Glasgow: Richard Griffin & Co. New edition with addition by Robert Etheridge and Harry Govier Seeley 1885 (reprint 2015 Arkose Press)

The Mountains, Rivers and Sea Coast of Yorkshire 1853 London: John Murray

Railway Excursion from York, Leeds and Hull 1853 York & Hull: Author (3rd reprint 1854 as Excursions from the North Eastern Railway)

Life on Earth its Origin and Succession 1860 Cambridge & London: Macmillan

Vesuvius 1869 Oxford Clarendon Press

Geology of Oxford and the Valley of the Thames 1871 Oxford Clarendon Press

John Phillips's Lithographical Notebook (edited by Michael Twyman) 2016 London Printing Historical Society

2. Other keys sources

Allen David Elliston (1976) *The Naturalist in Britain) – A Social History*. London: Allen Lane/Penguin

Baines, Henry (1840). *The Flora of Yorkshire* London: Longmans

Beck, Howard M. (1984) *Gaping Gill, 150 Years of Exploration London*: Robert Hale

Bairstow Martin (1990/2002) *Railways in East Yorkshire Vol 1*. Pudsey: Author

Brannen Peter (2017) The Ends of the World. London: Oneworld Publications

Buckland William (1823) *Reliquiae Diluvianae; or Observations on the Organic remains contained in Caves, Fissures and Diluvial Gravel and on other Geological Phenomena attesting to the Action of an Universal Deluge*. London: John Murray.

Buckland William (1836) *Geology and Mineralogy considered with reference to Natural Theology (Bridgewater Treatise VI)*. London: William Pickering

Chambers Robert (1844) *Vestiges of the Natural History of Creation*. London: W&R Chambers

Clark John Willis and Hughes Thomas McKenny (1890) *The Life and Letters of Adam Sedgwick*. Cambridge: Cambridge University Press

Cockburn William Dean of York (1845) *The Bible Defended against the British Association*. London: Whitaker

Darwin Charles (1859) *On the Origin of Species by Means of Natural Selection*, London: John Murray

Elgee Frank (1912) – *The Moorlands of North Eastern Yorkshire their Natural History and Origin*. London: A. Brown & Sons

Hemingway J.E. and Rayner D.H. (edited 1974) *The Geology and Mineral Resources of Yorkshire*. Leeds: Yorkshire Geological Society

Hogarth Peter J. and Anderson Ewan W. (2018) *The Most Fortunate Situation – the story of York's Museum Gardens*. York: Yorkshire Philosophical Society

Howarth O.J.R. (1931) *The British Association for the Advancement of Science: A Retrospect 1831–1931* London: BAAS

Joy David (1969) The *Whitby & Pickering Railway* Clapham, Yorkshire: Dalesman

Kendall Percy Fry and Wroot Herbert E. (1924) *Geology of Yorkshire – An Illustration of the Evolution of Northern England*. Leeds: The Authors

Morrell Jack (2005): *John Phillips and the Business of Victorian Science*. Aldershot: Ashgate

Myerscough Richard, Wallace Veronica (2016) *Famous Geologists of Yorkshire*. York: PLACE

Orange A.D. (1973) *Philosophers and Provincials. The Yorkshire Philosophical Society from 1822–1844*. York: Yorkshire Philosophical Society

Osborne Roger (1998) : *The Floating Egg: Episodes in the Making of Geology*. London: Jonathan Cape

Peacock A.J. and Joy David (1971) *George Hudson of York*. Clapham (Yorkshire) Dalesman

Pyrah B.J. (1988) The History of the Yorkshire Museum and its Geological Collections. York: William Sessions

Raistrick Arthur (1970) The Making of the English Landscape: West Riding of Yorkshire. Hodder& Stoughton: London

Raistrick Arthur, Illingworth John L. (1967) *The Face of North-West Yorkshire*. Clapham, Yorkshire: Dalesman

Rubinstein David (2009): *The Nature of the World: The Yorkshire Philosophical Society 1822–2000*. York: Quack Books

Rudwick M.J.S. (2008) *Worlds before Adam: The reconstruction of Geohistory in the Age of Reform* Chicago: University of Chicago Press

Rudwick, M. J. S. (2014), *Earth's Deep History: How It Was Discovered and Why It Matters* (Chicago: University of Chicago Press).

Scrutton Colin (ed) (1994) *Yorkshire Rocks and Landscape: A Field Guide* Maryport: Ellenbank Press/Yorkshire Geological Society

Sedgwick Adam (1833) *A Discourse on the Studies of the University*. London: John Deighton; Cambridge: John Parker; 1969 (5th edition reprint with Preface by Sir Eric Ashby and Mary Anderson Victorian Library. Leicester: Leicester University Press

Speakman Colin (1982) *Adam Sedgwick Geologist and Dalesman*. Heathfield, Sussex: Broad Oak Press; New edition (2018) Hebden Bridge Gritstone/ Yorkshire Geological Society

Waltham Tony (1984) *Caves, Crags and Gorges*. London: Constable

Waltham Tony (2007) *Yorkshire Dales Landscape and Geology*. Marlborough: Crowood Press

Winchester Simon (2001) *The Map that Changed the World*. London: Viking Press/Penguin

Photocredits

British Geological Survey (Geoscenic Asset Bank) pp21, 73, 95, 157, 158, 163; Dr Andy Howard, pp 9, 56, 59, 69, 114–5, 122; History of Geology Group p11; Ingleborough Cave pp129, 177; National Portrait Gallery p7; North York Moors National Park Authority pp180, 182; Oxford University Museum: cover, pp139, 153; Peter Woods p27; Royal Society p87; Scarborough Rotunda Museum p58; Stump Cross Caverns p43; Tom Lord Collection pp161, 162; Walking Englishman (walkingenglishman.com) pp22, 67, 132; Wellcome Institute p35; Yorkshire Geological Society pp35, 175; Yorkshire Museum pp39, 61, 63, 118; Yorkshire Wolds Railway p143.

Other images are taken from Wikimedia Commons and Creative Commons, out of copyright sources, plus copyright images by Dorian Speakman and the author as credited.

Index